GRASSE 3/23/66

by the same author: *The Martlet's Tale* (1966)

GRASSE
3/23/66

Nicholas Delbanco

1968
J. B. LIPPINCOTT COMPANY
PHILADELPHIA / NEW YORK

To my mother and father

Dionysus, god of the Orphic mystery cult, had three incarnations, the second titled Zagreus. Son of Zeus and the raped Persephone, Zagreus, an infant, grew enchanted with earth and descended to play. The Titans, enemies of Zeus and incited by the jealous Hera, spied the child, fell upon, dismembered and ate him. Zeus, grief-stricken, destroyed the cannibals with thunderbolts, but from their glowing ashes sprang the race of men. Man, therefore, embodies both godhead and the criminals who once denied and murdered him. The orgiastic rites of the Orphic religion stem from the belief that each living man contains a piece of Zagreus, and that through the frenzied, drugged communion of initiates, Dionysus is once again restored, made whole.

Orpheus, the sun-singer, high priest of the cult, shared Zagreus' fate. After the second loss of Eurydice, he retired to a mountain to ponder doctrine and his sorrow, but was in turn dismembered by the Maenads, votives of a rival sect. His head then floated to the sea, still singing Eurydice's name.

1

ORPHEUS AND EURYDICE

Waned, I wined and, whining, wound my fingers hundredfold, found hair. A single strand encumbers, and you leave me limp who, single-legged, weaves to whimper: *tu m'a laissé*. Malaise: wounds, wounds—the plush fruit palls; footfalls mush lush grape into reasons; fool. I drove back here bereft. As it lay in my power, I sang. A chicken settled clucking on the coal; our meadow seemed a green sheep shorn of hay. The bells ring out abandon, and I am alone. I shall attempt to trace you, body forth the loss, but have no least hope of success. (Success, surcease; abandon hope, sir, cease, as you alone are left. Desist from the diseased deceased; from sheer tedium of this *te deum* I am gone mad with words, with grief. Christ wed those women as they could not bear; go, get thee to a nunnery; nones ring.) Where once your black coat hung is white, and strung to memory I find one yellow hair. I loved you past imagining yet left you on the plane. I lock the door behind me and I cannot understand. (Cart, horse, keep your hot hand on plow, your wand up now, with carrot and with stick, with switch, with swatch, watch how the beasts plod sod, purr, sue me sir across the sea, see how we dig to die today, a horse before the heart.) I too, I too was beautiful, a youth. I also sang the sun awake and nimble-footed, fleet, would dance among the Pleiades, could kick my heels and click. The sweet snows go; things change. In the rock-strewn, ill-lit center of the hills, descending from Gourdon, braked near the quarry and scattering dust, the limestones huge above me and the sun sea-drunk, I looked to the left, Astrid, to a little frame hut, receptacle of managers where yet an oil lamp, unillumined, swung, and, framed by the skeletal door, slat-crossed, accentuating vacuum, dark against the inner dark, I saw an old man hover, wave, and knew my father dead. A special man went common, gold brick turned to clay—a manger ran to mange. Let us shift tense (as must the Bedouin: within the desert, camel-backed, we sift like straw in wind); I know my father died. Winnow the chaff from grain; reap grim, encyclical; he faded with the crowing of the clock. Perhaps I have been happy here because of dogs; this, the world's one place where I have not been followed, sniffed, pariah to the poodle, stranger to the snuffling chow. Tailless, the slop, sleep-filled beasts thump at me here, and I am at home. (Love is a long-time falling; filling is a long-time love. If ever eye prove false to you, black hand shall seem white glove.) How are we sick with rhythm, beaten bush, and beer: for I remember asking, in Geneva, once, after a disappeared uncle, concluded long dead, a displaced person, prisoner, last heard of in Papenburg, 1941, by telegram from Heidi Rosen signaling his health (which took three years to be delivered and came via Bombay, he, a professed Moslem, machinist) and being ushered into archives, hall of death, hope, cowardice, the International Red Cross, with heroism listed, fate upon a yellow card, my family indexed and uncle six sad dots. There, the would-be-forgotten slide ever-remembered beneath some custodian thumb. The escaped, shot, imprisoned, the gassed and surrendered are catalogued there, ranked in file. Here the long rows of dead leaves still clinging to oak are as cards in that windless one room. Here, blown leaf turns to paper and on it I can but inscribe: not forgotten, dash-dash-dash, contact wife.

14

A book about indulgences: announce me at the door. Marakei, Malaita, Onotoa, Nanomana, Lord Howe, Nui, Nukufetau, Funafuti, Vunisea, Nukualofa, Atafu, Guam, Sarigan, Agrihan, Asuncion, Ascension, Kita-iwo-jima, Garapan, La Palma, Gomera, Fogo, Praia, Platte, Coetivy, Nias, Lahewa, Tamana, Kiska, Umnak, Seguam, Amlia, Onekotan, Kure, Manihiki, Anguilla, Fernando de Noronha, Angatau, Ngatik, Jaluit, Ebon, Brabant, Montague, Andros, Poros, Flores, Eauripik, Ifalik, Epi, Merir, Tahanéa, Haraiki, Reitoru, Hikué, Morotai, Aki-Aki, Oeno, Fanning, Eiao, Motu-Iti Tínos, Mansel, Prince Patrick, Vrangelya, Kyakhovskie, Rongerik, on any of these islands I could hide, would feel the sweet sea lapping and stay calm. I come instead to you—without alternative. (In the destructive elegant immerse; shipwreck with no trousseau. This floating island, probably misspelled and nonexistent, is my home; this bottle both tide and high time. Thrown coconuts split rock-struck like my life; the molting monkeys chatter at the track. Bananas grow, fall, grow, constructive aliment, and I, with white eyes, weep. Lies: my eyes are brown, I have not cried in years. I sit here in the South of France and must begin again.) This paper comes from wood, from pulp. Wood comes from dead trees. I write upon dead trees. I catch the word on winding sheets: Astrid, my wife, loved the wood. Inconclusive is the beast that bites his tail; men drive their trucks beneath me and the foundry echoes smoke. Come, commiserate, commingle, flesh and flesh are joined. For advancement, a future, duty, illusion, or profit, loss, a drink, a dollar, memory, for mammary, the past, from pride, for proof, from weariness, for reassurance, fear, fun, fur, rings, sleep, compassion, ease, itch, heat, from sympathy, from habit, usage, need, for francs, a ruble, rubble, rub, six hundred drachmas, mark, a guinea, thousand-lire note, in earnest, secret, and in any bed at all, on

15

floor, field, standing, sitting, cooking, by the kitchen sink, in clubs, at wakes, on Sunday, in telephone booths and on tables, in cars, a trice, truce, tryst, we copulate, capitulate, rot, rut. Animals with antlers locked, kidney to kidney pressed, wolves in the clothing of sheep, a pig in a poke, a needle hidden in hay, I say let marriages perish and wither, a rooster with no head is lust that climbs upon yon clucking hen, for sport, spite, spent, and rats raise their legs, lie to die, decline, recline, I think of a train carriage, unlit, uncoupled, in a shed, and the hard seat sperm, sputum-covered, scratching her bent back where lights flicker twice to reveal his blue conductor's uniform well folded on the floor, a copy of the *Daily Mail* containing sandwiches, her high hat toppled and each knot undone, I think of a river, cigars, and prophylactics stretched, to small boys seeming fish; the tin foil glistens by the mayonnaise, the lettuce and ox tongue, babble on, the tunnel of love a dead end, and arrogant he rides to come whence once he came, enter, inter, I cannot dignify it even with alliteration, mindless, driven, by the waters, lost, we bare to bear in pain, and at this hour how many may in the dim city die, wither, fornicate, weep, extinguish the light with a blind, how many bedsprings come unstuck and stockings rip to run, how many bottles break for slaughter, multitudes submit. Upon a street corner I stand, digging the universal flux, the tattoo of your soles. This ceaseless rhythm has crazed me; staccato, stiletto, eye falls at your feet. I am no longer whole; do raise them once again, point heel, hem, toe to the sky, and resurrect me altogether, for whatever reason, for love. (Old men look like women and old women, men; gravediggers, considering angles, widen the bottom and top. Coffins slide on the diagonal but sometimes stick constricted; they therefore take the drill and widen the sides of the pit.) Hurakan, the storm god, broke the beach and land

16

asunder, sucked the swordfish boats like sugar into his hot bay, splintered barns and sent them bobbing, slaughtered sheep and trees. Throughout that storm we lay at peace, and now, the east wind gentled, I am torn. Must we shriek mismanagement in some stage setter's ear; what curious designing does he deign to show? Is there no correspondence in an outside gale, no mirrored actuality without? We must attempt to emulate the wheat; Hurakan split lobster boats like lobster, spat. My wife and I drove from Milano to Grasse; in the foothills behind Valbonne, we found a house and stayed. A year after arrival, our marriage broke; she left. I know it necessary to describe the house but find it difficult; how say to the inquisitive, this is where she sat? (Two shutters for each window; a front room and a back. In this house once the sheep slept, quiet, and a shepherd piped.) Upon the wall you note a hieroglyph of need. That, madam, denotes, demarks the half-consumed melon I threw at her face. The acid stain of splattered seed, a testament and litmus left immersed. (While there in the corner we used to keep plants, and possibly you shall—oh leave untouched the bench she swept and spread upon for joy.) My little lawyer's blind mind cries: *caveat emptor*, the wood is wormholed now. My wife was twenty-six years old, and I but twenty-eight; we had been married three years. This fuse blew once before, once only, in high wind, and then these candles helped. (A grandstand empty, a bar padlocked, no one on the tennis courts, nobody in the pool; Italian opera blares from the Zenith on the masseur's table; there is no masseur. There is the massive error, merely, of a game concluded when we did not know the rules. Each community of polyps is better versed than we.) Love is the single therapy that works; I climbed the stairs palm upwards, penitent. Before the accident, I had been world-renowned. Absurd: there never was an accident, there never was a world—but only her, here, her. Spurt, swart Philoctetes; may thy bow resonate; drink not of unmixed wine. In intermittent clarity, a lucid ragged exit light with intermission rung, I sit upon my tailored vestigial tail and (like the vanished fair this work, the week-end ferris wheel and carousel and fortune booth, the shooting gallery, ringtoss unstrung, the prize cow picked, the hawkers packed, departed, deported, pink polar bears crated and neon un-plugged, signs blank, each connection severed and the meadow stripped, one little boy left penniless to suck his final all-day sucker, succor, hear the thunder) clap. A dose should be treated by pencil, lacking penicillin: ease disease. All the world's a cage, and all the men and women merely pliers: bend elbows at a bar, throw bar belle bottoms up; *salud y pesetas y pay.* Don't we play for the things, for the thinks that we do; yes, isn't it nice to sink so? The theater is my life; pancake has battered my face. I tread the boards, floored, gored, as dying swan-swain swoon. The curtain cannot fall too soon (and life, time's fool, etc.); I shall fain feign a sneeze. Diffident yet dissident, there is a madness in my method, top to my head, bent neck. Dream of the rod, the rood: come and thread my needle, said the gallows to the rope: stage sage. I think with fondness of, nostalgia for the mildly maniacal friends I have made, menagerie unringed. Parade before me now, I com-mand, commend you, just a little out of step, fool's-capped, and to your private beat. Alfonso, the huge Swede, formerly a weight-lifter, bully, pimp, poseur, with thin furled umbrella and muscle-man shirt, with sweat pants or zoot suit and uncut cigar, karate belt worn as a tie, his white bangs streaked, dyed red, awoke one day to find a boil upon his upper arm and telephoned me, terror-struck, convinced of cancer, gentled, the mountain of his tricep surmounted by black flag. From that

18

sunlit morning he knew no more rest, but lay upon his nine-foot bed, curled, cowering, cutting up newspaper ads, a Christian Scientist, initiate, pillbox, and medicine man ("Fear not, Alfonso," said the doctor, "I am God's messenger come here to save you"), great trunk felled by the breeze. The boil went away, but mortality remained; Alfonso walks the New York streets, meek, thermometer stuck to his tongue, body bent beneath the two-pound placard he bears, a light cross too heavy for him, his shoulders and pectorals laid waste with doubt, predicting the bubonic plague. I have seen him jump, a gangling mass of ganglia, on tables for fear of a mouse, or shy his copy of Camus in corners after rats. Waving his banner before him in alleys, garbage cans, at roofs, he weathers the conditional, screams "If!" Madame de la Peight, blue-haired and fifty-five, a yoga, yogurt addict and tap dancer still, deserted ship, who married Mr. Pate and fruit-juiced him to death, a vegetarian, insistent, who offered him carrots when he, at sixty-seven, collapsed from standing on his head, from malnutrition, lack of hope, who bought black contact lenses when she was in mourning and at her term a gauntlet glove, drives her new blue Cadillac with windows closed all summer, the windshield wipers on and wearing rain hats, fur, opens the car when it's winter, or rains, then leaves it at her garage, the leather and carpets awash, the metal rusting, to be reserviced, pitied, scrubbed, enters her wide hall burdened with cucumbers. "Mustn't, must we, be enslaved to the elements," she says, "it's elementary, what, son, nor to machines," then cartwheels twice while I collect the fallen Confederate change. I think of Thomas Irving Alexander Washington Snopes Smith, the most beautiful Negro I know, hophead and forty-eight, black to the other's red, blue, white, a warlock, juggler, mime, who looks but half his age and will stay permanently ten,

19

pickled, preserved, the community's charge, in his own snow palace king, execrable poet, great roller skater, monocyclist, hero, mask, who buys a coffee malted and empties bottle after bottle in it, stirs with a quill pen and drinks deep for joy. "I just come from Rome," he insists, and carries a suitcase wherever he goes—"Rome is home, man, me and Michelangelo." He was born in Chapel Hill. An absolute beacon, son of a deacon who brought home the bacon to pilloried post, and "haste makes hate," he says, Thomas walks into Boston from Cambridge for meals, then back again to sleep. I saw him on the cover of the London *Sunday Times*, dressed as a woman, bearing balloons, selling poppies, smelling salt, exampling America's poor. Clowns, clowns, perturbed, rest: I am the one gone wild. (Who also can remember having once seen this: "The Orpheus C. Kerr papers, being a complete contemporaneous military history of the Mackerel Brigade: its unparalleled strategical exploits on land and water and unprecedented struggles for the Union. . . .") For two days now the sole coherent sound inside my skull has been your name, a treadmill and an unplumbed well, Astrid, the fluttering bird of my throat noises soft captive songs to the sky, professional mourner myself, benumbed, and every sin remembered, none redressed: I cannot, till redemption, cannot fail to feel. Memories obsess me, of our delighted past, the village where we lived all our first married year, a little village, sea-swept, off the coast of Maine, a fisherman's shack our excuse for a house, three rooms defenseless under rain, the rafters sloping crazily and the one door askew. Deer tracked the salt lick; Astrid sang. We could have lived contented then inside a wet tree trunk. The shingled roof grew mushrooms, and squirrels signaled dawn. We showered according to sun, told time by its light in our room. A small stream wandered by the door, brought leaves, mosquitoes, mud. Two derelict refrigerators banged their lockless doors in storm; a 1930 Cadillac stood green, stripped, motorless. We came in spring, stayed through the winter, left; I went for fresh fish daily, yellowtail, bonita, bluefish, fluke. I gathered mussels, quahogs, scallops in the winter, watched the herring run. The one store ordered crepes suzette and cognac at our wish. The fishermen would leave us lobster, or a swordfish slab, and ice. I fished by lying on the dunes and looking out to sea; where gulls collected, or bass broke the water, I cast. On summer nights we swam. I cleaned the catch and brought it home; the elms were lit with oil. (Women carry bread sticks and olive branches, bend; a motorcycle, detonating, dies. The country is encumbered with these hills. Fantasy home never finished, a villa perches on steel pilings by Le Loup. I shall write a strophe to catastrophe, a eulogy and elegy, lament the lie that breeds no daughter, ply my fruitless pillar wife with salt.) We attempt to arrogate some province as our own and allocate the remnant world to others with relief. Were I but the single ruler of my heart and head, had I absolute supremacy in yours, uncharted regions might remain unmapped and I would know no waste, feel none the poorer for the flag yet furled. All true homes stand recognized at once. Each forest is primeval, offers Eve and hemlock, shakes the most Socratic certainty with night. What troubles me above all is, Xanthippe, you. The innocent arrangement of that plant lies broken, and the deep design seems lawless, cruel, cut. I long for ordination, patterning, belief; the crumbs we strewed behind us were devoured by a crow. Sophistry can soften but cannot eradicate: that black-winged bird pursues us, and we are alone. (A woman, short, and elderly, parades behind her dachshund every afternoon. What fierce, leashed bondage they portray, she licking and he snapping, choke-collared, beaten, sleek. Iseult of the White Hands

21

is she who haunts the hall, a technicality depriving her of solace, misery her portion, that potion a miser's excuse.) Between the random and the rigid, there must be somewhere harmony; beyond the counterfeit, a modal-model, fact. I have seen the body of a white bird black with flies, seen the sparrow hawk, immobile, glide in air. Each thing holds its opposite, contains its own negation; I make motions, still, that need yours to complete. Wanderer, do you not know the woods give ceaseless shelter, that Astrid's accidental mention is still the loudest sound? When my stomach takes no notice (*Dieu, que le son du coeur*), all shall be absolved. Anemone gives way to poppy; get with child mandragora; nor may we share November, the last leaves. (Orpheus, for his defection, was torn apart by vengeful womankind. Or do the Thracian maids but represent a cocktail party; he, the poet there? He sang, and Tantalus stopped thirsting, "Death, remember Love." Herons flew to listen at the water where his dead head mourned; rushes bent to hear.) Let us consider next the light-eyed girls on motorcycles, vague, unwashed, a BMW between their shaken thighs, either too old or too young, breasts udderlike or undersized, straight-haired, wearing Mexican beads and a muumuu, or slacks, slack, psychoanalyzed, and I remember lying on a New York bed, the city spread beneath me, its East River tugboat-tamed, a girl called Harry beside me, a lesbian, Harriet, and this her little room above the Midtown Tunnel, yellow, the lights off, she weeping undressed, and I collected clothing, left; a woman stopped me on the street, wearing red, turbaned, forty, bobby-socked, chapfallen, cried, "A & P, now don't forget to pee!" I twiddle toothpicks with my teeth, I am forever asked by children, "Are you Irish, mistair, no?"; I am lust-ridden, yes, lost, worked in a mental hospital once with six women patients whose problem was men, who scratched their stomachs watching me and followed drooling where I walked; all I had ever wanted was a little Harley, Triumph, peace, a bit of wind to brake, and bread: a leg of lamb, jug-jug. On the southern side of the valley, in a grove of cyprus, on a slight rise, facing west, a huge gray mausoleum stands, colonnaded, circular, uncompromised by ivy or by light. The red bulbs meant to stipple it at sunset all are smashed. Lovers come to lie beneath the tended trees, paint initials on the marble steps, mock the widow Desmouline with wine. Owner of two hundred fertile hectares, she had had the grave erected for her husband, childless self. Foul and prodigiously rich, she lived till eighty-three. At her death, the peasants danced, heard a wild dog howl. (Bushes burn with autumn and we walk again through pine woods, strip a branch of needles, smell your scented hand. Shame is but the memory of innocence undone. I wanted to tell you the birds sing above and, turning—forgive—saw you fall.) Let me not to the marriage of true minds admit. Impedimenta and impiety run rife; the lawyer of the widow Desmouline administered, as willed, ten thousand francs to each of the peasants who came to her funeral—did she turn to charity or scorn the people still? As she was hated, and it was December, and the reward not previously publicized, only three mourners arrived. (Rose beds shall nestle nettleless beneath your back, Astrid; the cosmic cosmetic shall cover you quite; not with a bang but a whip-her, the bedsprings contrapuntal, we shall enter once again that spiral of dependence, a minuet of the minute, a melancholy organ grinding to cacophany, interlocked ascension in the scale of need, a scorn of proud man's contumely and poor tumescence both.) The final supper eaten lies heraldic in my mind; no single word remembered, but the diptych holds. A one-eyed cat, black succubus, pranced to the table, begged. With flagons of *vin de Provence* at your wrist, with broken crust strewn where the cat sat to lick, a chicken bone protruding from beneath my emptied glass, with peas, with tarragon and parsley patterned on your inner arm, no noise, the rivulets of water navigating flesh, mascara-laden, miniscule, with every piece of meat gone cold and palm leaves on the floor—I offered escargots; and you commenced to cry. We paid pilgrim's respect, when first wed, in Maine, to the derelict brickyard, a wilderness walled there, fantastical dream of a dead wagoner, his mission miscarried and in ruins then, four kilns that could fire the sky blasted, bent, the waterwheel rotted and pulleys rust-ringed, the torrent that worked it a trickle, a stream, gray feces of owls where once clay baked to brick. The cliffs there are clay, and the coast line not difficult; he had envisioned barge ferries shunting, his four kilns supplying the schools of Augusta, a market from Ellsworth to Kennebunkport. Two ferries split, sundered, that winter, on rocks; ice covered the cove and deep snowdrifts sank huts. The wagoner burned to his death and was ash. Reclaimed, the field sprouts ivy now, and tendrils twine to pipes. Eighty years useless, three smokestacks collapsed; the road to the brickyard stands wired, mined, blocked. The wagoner's granddaughter, crazed with her legacy, fires on sight; we walked from the harbor three miles by stone beach. Kelp and Clorox bottles, barrel staves, masts, hoops, skeletal fish littered the wharf planks; the blue bay was calm. Testament to failure, nest for the seabirds and mice, a frozen succession of flaws, the aqueduct emptied to air. (In his sonorous gentility wrapped as a fly in spider strands, desperate, immobile, fixed by gossamer, Anatole grew beard, mustache to counteract that other beard, the laughing toothless lips he hated and his mother's underarm. Elephants tossed nightly when she crossed her legs to look for sleep; Anatole, at forty-seven, kissed her pillowed wig and waited, saw a strung fox, beagles yapping, father shot and each wound dressed.) Men thresh grain and horses pull the plow in circles, figure forth our energy and aimlessness, turn the grass and earth to profit, reap the discord sown. You have learned to leave me and I am but rancid leavings, residue of previous community, an anchor with no craft. Lungfish swirl and eddy where the chain links, broken, gape. (In 1923, with portraits of Madame Blavatsky and John, titled *Oil as a New Medium*, Serge Triapin, the fabulous painter, child prodigy, showman since stale, health faddist, lover, knight, charlatan, priest, commenced to draw society, made relics of constraint. When the others were Japanese, he had been Indian; when others went cubist, Triapin drew spheres. It was he who revived the egg tempera tint. A draftsman nonpareil, and also good at darts, he resides now, surrounded, in his villa at Vence. Come into my parlor, said the spider to the fly; looking back it is clear that marriage, work, year were splintered, jetsam when he raised his glass, on rocks.) To be a firewarden, merely, somewhere west of Suez, north of Ashford Junction, scanning the June sky, glass-walled in my high hut, the flyers dropping ale, and mail, and *Paradise Regained,* red streamers trailing steak as it torpedoes down, uncertain as to fixed smoke blown, the lumber mills to south, and mists from the Pacific sometimes finger-thick, and sheep raising dust there seem smoke, to stand upon the glass-legged stool to watch night lightning hit, to radio in readings and to watch the second ridge—I could eke eons out like that, composedly, repose. ("Taste the cream, Ah can taste the cream," chanted Davey McKintyre, frugging, in his club, the third-best second-story man in all of Soho then, adrift in ice, tobogganing, clad in pin-stripe pink parachute silk, his five-foot-four extended to a true six-footer's scarlet lip, and she, his molded mannikin, unbending, bit the hand, and next they played *Erotica,* and butch banged spring with butch, a finger in a diesel dyke, while inside of an olive I saw Porky Pig. Standing forlorn at the right of the page, dressed as Petunia, his tan vest too tight, fleeing from gangsters, casting a single long shadow down streets, unable to stammer his high-pitched "H-Help," looking fearfully over his shoulder for knives, the curlicue escaping rear from gingham, calico, he dominated gin—a woman pulled a woman's wig and all hair came undone, revealing green clipped stubble on the skull, Delilah shorn in turn. . . .) With pebbles in my mouth, however, hand upon my chest, right leg spaced slightly back for balance, crocked head cocked to left, orotund, rhetorical, confounding the phrenologists, I pass the time of day. Speaking in measured screams, noting the Greenwich Mean Time, calibrating Noumea some eight hours removed, we register the sand. Perhaps this lack of sequence comes as consequence, notes at the last that are beginning, commencement interspersed, the seasons spread within my work like leaven, leaf by leaf. Doubled back on the spirit's spent track: a foxy quarry, startled deer—where mountain goats still claim dominion, mounting larks should sing. Most archetypical of journeys, arching hoopoe whirled without end, no angle of incident equal to refraction, refractory, I saw—the miracle of flight a ceaseless wonder, watched stewardess grab at the joy stick to pull, weightless, weightless, weightless, she shifting into gear, saw suddenly the Esterel a hillock pressed to sand, and Nice a needling petit point, and Giens a dropped stitch, pearl, ascended through the blanket clouds this cotton-candy world (a seat at Cheapside Circus, clown, buy me for forty cents, the fine and dandy, daddy, sky), and balancing for purchase in my slanted cockpit, ring (Ringling alone has seen Beauty Bear), saw mist congeal upon the glass, myself securely cinched, the blue-green sea displaced by gray, one smuggled item, me, saw New York so concretely there that once was but a dream, where once a carriage spattered mud and snuffling sows would root, where Pegleg Peter used to walk the truckers tarry now, and swooping down to Kennedy I knew myself afraid, found comfort in the motion, merely, nose pressed to the pain (as when my childhood fear insisted robbers come by night, and mostly through the window and it's best to be prepared), dreamed no one at the airport with my inner eye gone blank. (Attend next to the bright-toothed youths, eager, athletic, Lothario-like, rimless glasses worn to tennis, address book buttoned down, perennial students, stock-market players, predictable, unkind.) Fog has settled, seems our true condition; space illusory and each man a chrysalis, quiescent, shroud-wrapped, sole. What creatures we might have been once; what creators we still strive, breaking, to be. I would give all my cocoon world for one clear sight of you, for one continued vision of fidelity. There were so many reasons—none of them sufficient, pile the pyrrhic pyre higher—and you had to go. "Canst thou guide Arcturus with his sons; behold now behemoth." (No one cares to sing about the sordidness of loss, sweet self-deception of a backwards look, and all the little bargainings of fear. I am Orpheus; I care.) Consider the meek of this earth, the lilies, festered, poor, turned far worse than weeds, a widow, a wallflower, or my friend John, six-foot-six and hairless, disinherited, horn-rimmed spectacles athwart his upturned nose, cuffs frayed and cuff links of rolled gold, Italian shoes and mismatched socks, eager, mistaken, sciatica-ridden, the silver of his fillings eternally on view, silk tie with a cellist inscribed, the best taropatch player I know, devoted to checkers and chess, egg head bent down across the board, a ping-pong sharper, fool; think of the endless iteration of hope, of next week, and the next, of all the bargains struck and each illusion kept, of soles marked *solde,* of Helen, bearded egotist, unkempt, a little lady lost within a too-large house, shawled, sheltered, parakeet addict and old shell collector, solitaire queen never crowned. Eating buttons, calling them peyote, spewing sewing thread as veins, we swallow bucketfuls of slop, anticipating ecstasy, root meadows for the sugar, fungus, morning-glory seed. "I am the true Napoleon," a man bearing placards proclaimed. "He who pays the piper names the tune." He who plays the piper danced the loon. Boots creased at his knees and his stomach distended, cocked hat cornered, fluttering, he circled the Rue de la Paix. Tired, tired, redoubt unfortified, I am now downed defenseless, walls beleaguered, siege-seized, tried. This is the height and depth of narcissism merely, a huge and private mockery of fact, a long and dismal treasure hunt around an elder's chair. I dream of pencil sharpeners and ink, amateur theatricals, gauze, cause. I strut across some private stage and mimic, for no audience, myself. Asbestos curtains hang in readiness; at the least hint of heat, they fall. Hand me my top hat and cane; the pit is replenished again. (In violet night, inviolate, knight-errant Randy practiced rapine on the supine, raptured and ravished each gal he had, impaled upon his sword all imperiled sisters in Christ, altered their habits habitually, martyred the heifer as well as the lamb, took Satan by the tail.) His two feet slightly splayed and big toe curving bent, right middle toe a trowel, the indentation of his heel more marked upon the left, long-legged, astraddle the high-tide sand slant, deep, rousing a chattering trail train of terns, his footprint familiar as mine—I followed or preceded the one other village king. Partitioned, the beach was our mutual fief, and, suzerains alike, with privacy our only bound, the bond between us, shore, down a mile stretch of strand we would bow. He, the alternative hermit, was, I heard, one afternoon, with kayak upturned, drowned, dead. The sea was calm and clear. Of all potential suicides that seemed the most disorganized, to paddle into sun, to fight one's long strong training and resistless sink (he could have swum to Nova Scotia hands tied to his back, but did not flutter, kick), like Crane, to fold a coat upon the rail and leap, and how that detail has disturbed, holds emblematic dominance, how the creased coat recurs. (Those who had their eyes put out were made to cross a stream, and if they did not stumble, could still pick their way, needles were inserted once again. There breathes no more creative artist than the torturer; imaginings, untrammeled, serve utility. How many ways to break a bone, how simple to destroy a spirit, bend the back and knee. Of all thy subtle stratagems, the most successful must be this: we hurl defiance at the foe, find nobody home but us chickens, and no response but air.) What, I wonder, would now happen were Astrid to return? First, formalities—but would I know her luggage, what new labels would there be, what continents between us added, spanned lands stuck to cloth? These thoughts are shameful, shame; have I requested, requisitioned, what I do not want? Would I continue writing, the rite of being written; could the book conclude? Geese emblazoned on the air and nets that swell with butterfish—in this city men wear matching ties and socks; in this city women wander girded against grace. Within the walled stone villages, upon some wind-whipped promontory, goats still scavenge, bleat. While still I can recall I shall call forth Astrid. On the night of her birth the sun set, signified a Capricorn; on the following day, it rose. A lovely large woman, a queen she appeared, the daughter of Eve and gazelle. In fact, there is true royalty in clouded Astrid's glory past; her grandmother was sired by a reverend august king—unhappily, however, not upon his wife. Illegitimate, the lass was wafted on a raft from shore, attended by

29

nursemaids, saved by Spanish fishermen; the nurses planked, the girl lay spared. Convent-kept in Mozambique, a black-haired beauty, frightened of water, forced to feint faints at the gardener's hut, carried away by the gamekeeper lad, beloved of Lawrence and each of the friars, sung to in sonnet and sick of her cell, our infant infanta escapes. Willful obfuscation of the record now; the needle waxes blunt. When next we spy her, she lives in Rome, wed, wealthy, bred to ardent ways; a duke in trade intrudes. Of that fateful narrow union bestride the Colosseum is Astrid's father sprung. He, a paradigm of learning, full-fleshed flutist, six-foot-four, sailed some *niña* to Plymouth, jumped ship. With curly black hair and brisk side whiskers, long Italian name and hope, this Cortez of Darien prospered in real estate, railroads, cigars, hitched his wagon to a star, a starlet, rather, and, with Astrid in offing, was wived. Transacted into bliss, the family stock and bond matured. Most immoderately married, they discovered dividends, and Astrid multiplied to six. She, the only one not wholly born of matrimony, carried the crass like a cross: I often have wondered if that unbroken line of bastards in her blood forbade her true children as if by tradition, made her, unwitting, unwilling to bear. Certainly, and from some foreign somewhere inside of my wife, a puritan purity ran riot, wild. Calvin streaked her horse to zebra, Zwingli wrapped her cow in cowl. I and my empty-headed leer were ever doused, soused by this daughter of flame; the convent vents tardy revenge. And that the sins of fathers are visited unto the fourth generation came clear; how frequently I cowered before that coward king. Trained to the *corps de ballet,* tutored in Providence, Utah, New York, summered in Bucks County where they owned land, a singer, a house painter, sportswoman, Dane, her mother was once in the films—an eighth-rate actress once. These are her reviews.

From *The Boston Guardian,* February third: ". . . and the supporting cast kept pace." From *The Christian Monitor,* September twenty-sixth: "A disappointing play, scarcely redeemed by its cast." Let him cast the first stone who owns a passport photo and a pair of tights. (Do you see these candle droppings wax opaque, this poor spoor spread to dust, these mementos, mild as pimiento, flake? A truce to my tracings, a plague on both horses, red powder on pie; your birthday letters lap written in water: *ad astra per* asperity, astride.) No single thing has changed. Six empty boxes strew the floor, the mop handle hangs minus head, I drink with Triapin, another beast has calved, another son has suckled, slept, Castor and Pollux wink above, I sit in laughing stocks. (A time to love, a time to lie, and three bags full with wool. Where is the word that you promised me, where; how have you pigpenned my pride? *Ad astra per aspera;* wait.) Paddling in my lethal Lethe, bourbon-and-branch-watered up to the gills, I see sunk loyalties and slipping down my sheet in technicolor see the faces, places past unreel unreal before me, sidle, slide. Marat in my bathtub with no knife intruding, a Shelley respired with no life protruding, kaleidoscope of character and catalogue of the good drowned (old Mr. Ebbeville, Harvard '17, fine hand with a sickle, handle-bar mustache, tennis sneakers worn beneath his overcoat, French wife, who swimming out beyond his depth came stingray-shocked to shore), I saw Charon's passenger list. All rites reserved, reversed; ferry cross the—mercy— Mersey; fog. Dim, in thee encircling, when we lay quieted, wreathed to each other and bound, surely I knew nations were relieved of gravity, no great weight pressed upon us able to oppress. All that once was natural now seems but decadent, a spiritual eunuch pulling down pants in the dark. Each act is automatic now that once took thought, took care: leash a *langouste,* strut the St. Germain, wear a fresh foulard per day. The moon is as a pebble dropped into the sky; ringed, it ripples outward, sets the world awash. Perhaps each private ghost is quieted at last, for eye can conjure spirits from the vasty deep but mind can do no battle with the air. I drove today toward Gréolières, aimless, plucked narcissi, stopped the car to lose myself on hill crests, in the stone shepherd huts, with brown trees stunted, rain barrels empty, rock patterning the pitted fields, a few flies collected on dung, and there upon a Druid wall I lay to conjure you. A single cloud scarred depthless sky, travesty of storm. Blue-painted women, broad-backed men had crossed their arms there, cried to the moon. How many have savaged their whimpering night wives on that stretch of lichen, of grass? Astrid, I cannot help but feel you lacked in charity. Perhaps the broken holy wall has taught me dimension, and sky. How little it matters; we die. A procession in progression, frozen frieze, ant colony, grave parliament of fowls; I am a small man, not two yards long, not two feet thick, uncertain, membrane and bone. We pass from sleep to sleep and slip the slope between. Learn license from the tides—those who depart, return; those who return, depart; and all is as once was. I lay diaphanous, unheeded by the foraging birds, and knew my puny place: mist risen on a pool. (Envision Colonel Billingsley, unmarried, forty-eight, an expert on Greek statue coloration, knots, scion who spends birthdays still at New Orleans, his home, inordinately shy, school tie immersed in soup, a little jar of honey in his overcoat, who found, on troop maneuvers, south of Istanbul, a piece of pottery, its origin unknown, that sheared his mind to shards and seared it with magnificence, hypotheses of Homer or the Hittite kings, enslaved his scholar spirit and enchanted it with mud. The Colonel has retired from the army and Akron, outfits expeditions and pursues his cache of clay;

fired with his first find still, he drafts a monograph—that was a paragraph, an essay, burgeons into book—on that twelve-inch oblong and drinks from its imagined spout in dreams. Comparison has taken him to London, Berlin, Cairo, Bonn, the prize encased in wrappings of the finest cotton, gauze, and while curators, outraged, gaze, he sweeps the desk of samples, shows the one true grail.) Bequeath to me the pride and comfort of believing that I did not mean to subjugate you so, that every grievance harbored is but memory of grief. I make no further effort to reveal or revel, ravel strands, look for some less simple story to repeat. Jack and Jill ate sprats, fell ill, and donkeys graze the lean grass, hill. How eagerly we jump at any new opinion of ourselves; there is no fortuneteller does not tempt, no cocktail conversation, when grown personal, that bores. How many turn toward astrology, analysis, pay for the pleasure of an undeterred discussion, treaty unilateral, someone bound to listen to their lecture, treat the treatise of their dream? When will we graduate to silence, legs interlocked in sun, not fright the little lizards at their play? Mortals have to seek for what they hapless find; each true disgrace is private, a platitude for attitude, but mine. "Man being in honour abideth not; how are the mighty fallen; we are but as dreamers of dreams." A constant falling off, consistent subtraction of joy, rank parasite called pity twined within the self, the past grown all-inclusive and the future, blank (consider the lilies, paradox of Mobil stations, how we wager age), my life is like a ship trip taken, the deck gull- and rain-swept, where buoys clink the drunkard's sound, a song of near submersion, soft, loud, soft, gong gone, and on some offshore shoal I watched a yawl sink, flounder, founder, washed awash on rock. This house that once was ours is now diminished, mine. The village recedes, is our desolate landscape, scrub pine and sage, vodka, dogs. (Prostrate on

33

account of his prostate, laid low in Ludlow, an engine of angina, catarrhal, doubly amputated, fifty-six, Kenneth could not look at ivy without shuddering, nor would the nurses let him suckle, slaver, savor their sweet tea. On a salver, as once with his tonsils, to this once-faultless Fauntleroy, they delivered ice cream, sundries, and, unsavory, Kenneth bent his tin spoon back. They wheeled him through the hall; he hexed adjoining doors; they offered him a socket and he played with plugs. Caroling his hardiness, warbling wealth, recovery, he caught his crutch in a circular door and splintered glass with wrists, returned to wet his sheets and watch the nurse proceed with dressing, will each wrong redressed.) It is this pimp and circumstance that has procured me woe; the origin of specie came when men divided work. Elaborate, we follow logarithms of set speech, search for a mate to decimate, a field to plow, prowess destroy. I shall costume myself as a *boulevardier; der Boden ist bedeckt mit Schnee.* Ribboned, I shall sally forth and dart gay brigand barbs on either side. Velveteen breeches will cover me quite; a primrose dangling from each ear will scent the shapely skull. Most utterly disintegrate, in dissipation's dissertation, chronic chronicle, in Domesday's tolling tome of doom, in stopped clock, sprung spring, epic of the epicure, a menstrual minstrel chants of chance. Loss grows impersonal, beyond specific referent; our falling off surpasses any height. My love is dyde, past potion's pale, I never shall see her more. To find her altogether faithless, distancing by furloughs of falsity, tissued in lie, my farthest thought, a trackless, racy waste to trace—why, that is past conceiving, enters into truth. Astrid was a whore. In her mind's eye, at least, it seemed better to marry than spurn. What's that smell like fish, mamma, tell you if you really want to know. Tumbled from up high, manna, bread has covered honey here below. The merest accident; I

34

met her friends, found out that she lied—with any boy baby
too cradled to rock. Hushed, sanguine, bloody blush-faced,
racked, I want no mere family more. Many, many take elle up
her sin; it was the writhing on the wall. That gets 'em every
time; a disembodied hand. She had been swayed in the balance
and found wanting—while Daniel sleeps indentured on a tiger
rug in den; these strokes are terrible things. First of all, allow,
they have a nasty habit of deforming you—or in the face, or in
the arm, or in the bend of the back. I am vaguely autistic and
mad. No antibody has yet been discovered to my ante-dote;
conjunction engaged in with no least compunction; Astrid, a
Hellion, has crossed to launch Paris, slipped ship, instructed to
abduct. I wished to hold her and apart—from that nothing.
Treu: a city gate-flung, gaped to trick; Odd and Sweet (Odd
y Süss), a hollow horse. That she was taken by night and in
check I am simply unwilling to brook. No knave or rook shall
stand while still I own bishop and king—go tell the duke of
France, *j'adoube,* he may touch the piece but not move. We are
not sundered quite nor hopelessly mated; his pawn has her but
en passant. (Men allay us, grief shall flame, and I, Agamemnon,
thee, city, sack. Posters for an undertaker trumpet: Rest Assured.) We make of virtue a necessity when representing hope;
the moral mortal takes his tea nor does not strew the table with
a pestilence of crumbs. Compulsive, convulsive, men die on
their backs; clustered birds burst into sunshine from the brown
treetops. I am rendered helpless by an unbound breast. (Heath
hens quiver somewhere free from gorse, and huckleberry turns
to flame with fall. Feet can leave no lasting mark in marsh;
know the deep monotony of mind. Scream reparation to the
sea; unaging intellect can catch no siren music with its ague.)
Come into my parlor, said the cockle to the cock. Botticelli,
vermicelli (*vero,* Michele?), Michael: blow your horn. Borne

into the undiscovered country from whose bourne—did you speak of country matters, miss? The Traveling Salesman and Tramp, a Farce for Fluke and Hoboe; Punch-drunk Judy Falls. Subtitled so to titillate; titter, will you please. Better late than never, says I, click hands, clap heels, *viva voce*, provoke. Alchemy increases the spiritual content of lead. All my proud progenitors are lying under hawthorne; weed has murdered grass. Gilt has framed my mirror, molds my varnished head; I had a friend who vanished, hope that has turned cheap. The little wet leaves whisper, what is lost stays lost. (Ripe oranges, wind-driven, fall; your image mocks me still. The girls of Opio bend, burgeoning, to pick, and I could share that harvest, sing my song anew. What furious perversion of loyalty is this, what shelf of granite garnered where the grain sheaves stand?) Ten years from now, whippet-lean, my future a glorious past, face furrowed with suffering, dignity, time, arrowhead welts on my left upper arm, mistresses jumping from roofs, knighthood hanging from brown neck, our name made famous and no longer yours, Astrid, I shall come upon you, the coarsened likeness of what was, grown limp from consorting with fools, teeth weakened, buttocks spread, chapfallen, two-chinned, great beauty gone bad—in some public place we shall meet, where the crowds surge, salute me, applaud. The darling of their every dream am I; I, to the descant, descend. Drums roll; brass blares. Midst murmuring multitudes then we shall move, dispensing doubloons, engulfed. The keys to the city are offered, accepted; fireworks blaze out farewell. And, at the exit, halting hosannas, holding another girl naked beside me, I shall kick you crying downstairs. (There is a cliff where springs create themselves from clay and where the spear grass shelters turtles, eels wash from the sea. Down a road that brooks no turning will you ever walk? We are acquainted with

the stars and innocence disconsolate, with hate—the sides of
wet stones cannot cure.) Set me as a seal upon thine heart; this
weal is unavailing; I am not shriven, free. In pure intolerance
of evil, Willoughby went mad. The sun that scored his eye
with distance creases petals still; concentric, eccentric, while
stars wink and glimmer, we crawl. Prepare, please, my bed
and my sheet; I have trodden the wine press alone. (There is
no artist living can depict this sky. Your sun is gone down while
it was yet day. Your mantle is a shell outgrown, rejected by the
tide. Rigor has unmanned me, and barbarity. Branches trace a
Chinese poem on the pool; we litter this earth like the hare.)
Let patience have her perfect work; this country is too lush. The
huge urn at the driveway's head toppled last night in wind.
Upon its shivered, splintered side it lay a more true mirror of
my cracked-clay self. Arid, acrid (even to Beersheba), stretches
the fruitless expanse; Cybele reduced to Sibyl spells from tea
leaves phrase-praise, fate. Drink dregs from this poor crucible
and steel yourself for fall. I am an inward oracle, full of foolish
counsel, relevant to nothing, drugged inanity. A chicken,
plucked and wrung, hangs dripping to the reed floor, tile; the
skull of a goat holds blood. Let patience have her prefect work;
ordain and prophecy. ("!I am—good—God? enlightened,
HUGE printed *Free* 7-page pamphlet reveals: numbers, the
body of, cigarettes, astronomy, salvation, faith, blackheads
cured with prayer, beatitude, & I WAS SATAN'S HORN!") To
catch a chipmunk, to demonstrate greed, place caraway seeds
in a milk bottle; watch. Mouth swelled with storage, it cannot
escape; lobsters eat dead fish. Triapin examples, stands ex-
emplar of success in our mink-ridden, televised, topsoil society,
hermit with pandering herd. Flattered and flatulent, ill-
mannered man, he is, you see, eccentric and wealthy, not
stubborn nor rude. Strange, how private childhood fears return

37

to haunt one's mock maturity; this silence deafens now as then. You are a massed miasma yet can hurt me still. The shadow of your shoulder darkens my least page; spent imagination does not spare. I thought millenium was sounded when we wed, the world would come to glory, and the nations, peace. Forsaking all others, I was but forsook. Priest, the plot sickens, thy words unavail. Content yourself with continents of continence; let be. When Adam delved (interstices of bottomless perdition, adamant), Eve span. Who was then the gentleman; what tailor stitched in time? Saving your worship, I have lost the thread, don't give a fig, would lief as well leave; nine worthies once took peacock vows: cry not about spilt milk nor irrigate gardens with salt. This ol' hammer laughs at antic anvils broke; this ol' anvil laughs—weigh sixteen poun' plus wood. Shards of meaning, merely, fragments off the proverbial fount, fond wisdom foundering, sound, echo in my mind, *ecco*, a thing of rags and patches, of bad lad songs and snatches, glad, a rivulet run dry. Parched for milk and kindness, high—"We have to be human," you wrote, as single signal and farewell—I wait. (Raveling my few poor strands and reveling, snip snip. That black, that green-eyed man, the Moor, grows dim beside empurpled me; wrung like a lacework handkerchief, ravaged, strung to envy, I fold with every Roderick, and there are legion, daily dainties, fairer-haired than I. Each Mussulmano, muscle man upon the street, each cockerel alive alive o is burnished furbishing of fear.) You lost your belt and left it here, your toothbrush, too, and isolation is a hook from which one raincoat hangs. See, I can grow maudlin with the best, I can go maudlin with the rest. I reread my diary notes; I have to believe I believed. The muse a jealous mistress is, and we enchained but chafe; ramshackled hand in cuff beneath the French links, gauche clasps, sinister, a pen. (*Ma muse, tu m'amuse.* I should like to thread you as a needle, whet my point.) Do you object to effort scatological or simply scattered logical effect? Nocturnal, the beast with two backs bellies out, and all things go bump in the night. The undertaker lays its eggs in animal decay. (Thrown into this *gouffre* we *souffre*, into this gulf we gulp. Desdemona entered in a brothel-low, expired on a high C, sank, took twenty curtain calls.) Knocked together in six minutes at the most (and to the ticking of the cuckoo hallway clock?), I am of special stock, *triste,* rammed into my mother's shanty, *Frauenzimmer,* frock. Connemara's cloth may be as cold as dawn— not to mention passionate, my father was no slouch, a second coming borne. Out of that small seed I poplared, popped, out of that burgeoning birch he raised cane. Ten commandments merely, and we cannot follow one; see how the good man must die. Divine aphasia is equally a phase; soon all shall be forgotten, ill-defined; "Why hast thou forsaken me?" he cried. (Clustering sparks from a log that will crumble are we in the heat of our hope. Into a roofed artesian well observe the raindrop drop. This morning I woke wreathed in blankets, saw the silver spindle of a butterfly. Coffee derives from the Arabic wine word; coffins deride expectation, attempt.) *Mea culpa, pater optime,* upon my knees, head, feet, and in other positions, sooner or later, laurel-heaped, cloven in clover, I have indulged in pride, wrath, envy, gluttony, lust, avarice, and sloth. Some, moreover, that I cannot remember just now: she was ugly as sin and quite as attractive. I lie. Consider the pigeon shoot in Delaware, five hundred birds released by gardeners, gray, mange-ridden surrogate doves, twelve of us standing upon the kempt grass, blasting with rifles and pistols and shotguns, on Easter Sunday, the white-coated drink bearers near, killing one hundred and twenty-six, then eating oysters, five hundred provided, four dozen eaten, and *foie.* I rode a tractor through the

39

land of my contractor friend, saw roads begun and stopped at trees, saw pipes, piles, jetties sunk, saw lakes in the making and pools. Tons and tons of peat moss lay leveled by barrow and crane. The village girls sucked thumbs and widened knees for us. Pernod we offered them, pernicious brew, with its telltale, its tall-tail effect. Many a maternity suit derives from that paternity uncorked. I lost a shirt stud in the hay and stained my cummerbund. May a cup patter oft in me; what a nice week end that was—another short story, dead end. (There have been long nights, moments, months, when, left expressionless, I put a face to fraud. More benignly, let us say I voiced an emotion, hoped therefore to feel it: envisaged a visage to be. I falsify to fortify; it's clear that sand castles stand best with cement. A rope trick, kindness, counterfeit, art—call it what you will, the final name is fraud.) If I thought you would read this, I never could write—how abject I am grown. The stickleback fish and the frog are better at courting than I. I tracked your huge name in the sand, and two gulls sat down on the D. I know I should go but remain, know this should stop but would take myself with me—and where? Into a peaceful place I'd walk, with olives above, doves alive, and each thirst slaked, gone slack. The planes from Nice are geese, broad-banded, winging home to home. Perhaps you crashed, bleach, blanch on a sandbar, all of your body gone bone; even now I could rejoin you, even yet return. The post office man is an unemployed actor, or deaf—I enter to ask for the mail; he scrabbles three minutes for form. The office is tiny, you've seen it, must know, with one window only and poured cement walls. He rings that cement with his voice; he sings out *"rien"* with a vengeance, a smile. "Monsieur n'a no thing hiss afterloon." The posters billow in his bellow, flap with his wind (while perhaps the water wreathes you, laps your enameled lip). I walk the sad way back; why do you not send word? A lame priest hops beneath me; dogs grovel in the shade. I go for mail each afternoon so that the gardener won't know you don't write. Where are the letters you promised; how are you comforted now—by plankton and polyps, by crabs? Have the piranha bitten you as I? And but for pride, protection, fear, we might not have parted at all. ("It's only that you leave me hopeless," Astrid said, "trust lost," and I tore triangles in leaves. "I am not, will not be," she said, "a character for one of your books," and meanwhile I was cataloguing gesture, tears, restraint.) The parable of Adam, Eve, would mirror no meaning were it without snake; the tree of knowledge grows critical here, and yet I do not know what happened, Triapin, nor why. That we are wailing cast forth I am certain, with garden soil spoiled I am clear. But the explanation, where?—I begin to recognize this sermon as inadequate, partaking too much of the mystery, *messe*, a priest who wavers, bibulous, blind, offering water as blood. Fold your hair about you; tear; we shall not rest again. Dogs are the children of decadence; my heart in this bone cage, diminished, rib-robbed, roasted, cannot cover yours. Terrible to be always necessary, never sufficient; the incorrect equation of our one and one makes two. A most asymmetrical marriage, a symptomatic asymptote; we should have been but unity, enough. Listen to the rhythmic, additive patois, the infection of inflection; I ravished the ravishing girl. Owls, rootless, hoot. In no sense innocent, the serpent as servant prevails. Try to elaborate, embroider, or explain; no use; we fell, the one irreducible fact, an element, no matter, embroiled, entailed, appositive, in the beginning an end. (At its mercy, onto rock, in water, under oak, we are as seeds of wheat blown by a river breeze. Thy rood and thy distaff are ever with me; from out where the sheep feed, for fear of loud laughter, in untutored him-hymn, I

41

praise.) In the Poldi-Pezzoli, Milan, on our first day, coming from Lanino, Rizzi, D'Oggioni, light, all the slow complexities of tempered tempera, entering the marble room where Breughel, Cranach, Teniers hung, within a *quattrocento* box of sandalwood for spice, I found some guard's straw hat. Black, interlocked, rimmed round with sweat, a mockery, it lay. (Pegged, stretched, scrubbed, expanded, nailed, wet, pink, taut and resistless to the stroke, oiled, linseed-smeared, washed, wide, I still can picture Astrid as a canvas by his couch. Kolinsky at the index finger daubs; Triapin bristle-brushes, touches her neck, nose. She sighs, and he enjoins her, silence, shapes her bit by bit—proceeds to rend her, render, past the pale of euphemism, invades both lap and lip. Behind, the storm clouds hover, hang; he interposes blinds—amongst the one-eyed, king. How could I so completely wink the loss of image there, my one wife captured, limned, bent to another will?) Just so, askew, within our year, witnessed by the eyeless statuettes, a detail detected, her face turned to flesh (what's wrong with this picture, pinpoint and win), a dolphin placenta on shore, heraldic, our harvest of salt—she breathed as he completed her, was his. Clouds scud across the sun, are gone; memory does not thus pass away. (How's that for seventeen syllables, *sensei*? How's this for thirty-four?) The year lengthens and its remnant dwindles; we have passed two sunless weeks; the mice are come inside. Solace in a solstice found: I sleep forty per cent of each day. Some soon time something has to happen, a god in a machine will summon me to drive. The oaks do not obscure the Pré-Alpes, are small shelter now. As teacups wait encased in acid, so am I encrusted with the leavings of departure, so is once-clear porcelain opaque. Even analogy fails. I shall wrap myself up in this cosy of air, dream of a crumpet, mix lemon metaphor, serve. (Perched on some high bar stool, the long-fluked fans above him churning, rum punch clutched in either hand and swizzle stick in mouth, white silk suit from Hong Kong stained with beer and bitters, slop, my friend Boittevin belches, weeps, berates the flies that cluster to him, pastes his canceled stamps. *"Feuilles o, sauvez la vie moi,"* he whistles, whispers, shouts. *"Petit moi malade,"* he snaps his residual button, pierces a nonexistent net, descends.) The sloe-eyed, slow-thighed ladies that I have not so far met succor, sway me nonetheless and sigh, conspiratorial, unmanned. Mountains I have never seen and yucca, thistle, palms wait tentative and shadowed; how many glade-gladdened maidens stretch themselves, expectant, see beyond their lid-lash prism, day. (Concatenation, color wash in an exploded skull; hummingbirds show fixity in motion, persevere. Still you hover, flowering, extract sleep-sweetness nightly, leave above my sheet the wayward petal stripped. Fold on fold unraveling, I can but dream your flesh.) At this remove, the bees incurious, the last rose fallen, my white hand brown, when cataloguing winter, I remember cold, the long March rains, the wood that I ceaselessly cut, stoked, the small hut sawdust-strewn, depleted coal, the silver of our painted stove caking, smoked, to black, trips taken with Georges to Gourdon, at five o'clock each Monday, Thursday, to deliver gas, his gray Renault immobilized in early morning frost, then choked and sputtering to start, the road from Magagnosc impassable for snow, and then the large trucks passed, and antlike we followed, laden with gas, in wake of their wheels, saw Le Loup an icicle beneath, and far away the sea, delivered, changed the tanks (and always he said as I helped, *"Mais non, monsieur, vous allez vous salir, ce n'est point necessaire,"* and always I would help), then *café au lait* offered by the patron; beating arms we berated the sky, reversed, the Alpes Maritimes cloud-covered behind, the sharp

43

curves thawed and rain-slick now, Georges navigating in second, swearing, cautious, proud, and I returned at eight, to Astrid still asleep, to radiators popping and a cat within the bin. (Even now, rereading, I cannot but destroy; no woeful lyric word rings true, and only this indifference obtains. I never loved her, never felt what yet I swear I swore; beyond the habitual, my masquerade. A shame to sham; listen, Astrid—a sediment of sentiment; no more.) Have you observed the alto-gether aged, how they shake, the separation of their speech and thought, that constant communion with self, grasped wine to warm bled blood, a fire burning even at midday, bones shrunk into their sockets and the flesh grown limp, epicene, or worse, still goaded by remembrance, sex-obsessed?—I am their youth-ful imitator now. When turning to my own so recent past, young kingdom of hope prematurely usurped, I find myself unable to decide—if it was glad and happy, or full of fore-boding, distress. My mother was a witch, or wondrous woman, which?—thus man can rewrite history, can recreate his child-hood origin. From Gaea we are come to Ceres, and the series (through lactating lovers and surrogate mammary) starts. My family has left me rich, a gentleman of leisure (with ascent on the left, with accent on the leman and the lees), and yet it seems far simpler for a camel to pass needles than water, to nestle in nettles, find haven, pleasure, than for me. What mockery is this, that I, enraged, can merely rag, and then a red rag weave and wave to no bull's eye? (What wanton soup to gourmand gods, what scruple-scrapple, offered mess are we?) It sometimes feels, and then a woman ought to somewhere weep, as if there is no rhyme, no rhythm whatsoever in this world, as if we spiral, spin to no one's pleasure, turn and turn. The spirochetes (Spiro-Shelley, Spiro-Byron) spawn, continue, and we persevere. (The proud plurality of light has waned with

winter, bowed to dark. It is now six o'clock, and every lamp—
my joy, a candle so brief it is Roman—switch switched. I sing
of notes in bottles, scraps scarified in wind. Georges says it will
not snow here, but I predict the snow.) Soft-spoken hangman,
murderer-thumbed, the scar on my cheek cruel, kind, I wear a
Spanish throwing knife; its sheath is my split heart. A complicated past: my ancestor Palinurus begat me with a mermaid
and streams of seamen interjected to occasion me. My father
was not what he seemed: a black prince, truly (no poor fruit
vendor allergic to peaches), unfairly deposed, and if I spoke
Swahili, I would bring him back—to power and glory and
mom. I was borne about ten thousand years ago, picked lint for
a living, slept like a sardine in cans. I was the John in nine
hundred Janes, cat-catcher, dog-pounding me. Cirrhosis of the
liver commenced in our hero at twelve, and syphilis, thirteen.
During the war, foxholed, I drank martinis for water, seeing
the wells were gone bad. A Zeppelin, blimp, balloon, a DC-6
or Piper Cub, anything that flies, a glider, Spitfire, stratojet,
they hop to my touch like a bird. Ask me if I'm C.I.A.? You
know I cannot answer that. What more do you desire, what
further sacrifice? Am I not homeless, rootless, misbegotten,
maimed? Have I not paid enough; must this begin again? Tears
run along the ridges of my nose; gray clamps holding the nostrils firm grow soaked. I too, I, too, was nimble-footed, fleet;
greet the sweet sun, will you, there's a lad. My clothes are
careful tweeds, my hair pepper and salt. Cigar smoke wreathes
me as a halo, obscuring my vision somewhat. Two donors kneel
on either side; by brass I have been framed. A complicated
man, yet comprehensible; refrain—roh, roh, roh your *bottes*
(gently down a down); my family crest and a shield. Beside
Curtmantle rode mine nuncle, fearless, emblazoned, anal
sphincter open, each valve disengaged. I am a proud man,

sensitive, and never could sell fruit. To think the blood of corsairs courses in this vein; I twiddle my sideburn in peace; I flex my foil, *épée*. I have married once only; that once was for all. ("Aristide ran after me," she said, "and I fell on a rock, hurt my foot." An easy text, not contradictory nor openly equivocal, yet from those words how I constructed split submission, joy. Reed pipes prolonged her pleasure and their rhythm was the goats'—Aristide, beekeeper, long-muscled, live accursed.) This is another morning, and the cock distends to crow. Sun sweeps the Esterel. Snow touches the top peaks like powder, lifting a crag face and smoothing crevasse cuts. Somehow some childhood echo comes to soothe my bent-kneed self— that all just prayers shall be answered, boons are bestowed if desired completely, and every petition goes granted, once read. Keep Faith: a truth beneath your pillow will transform to fifty cents. Perhaps frenetic prattle has meant but to fully prove this: I loved, love, can and shall. The sea is calm; today I think it true. Crickets compete with water pipes and are the only noise; the rest that silence is. Astrid, a vacuum filled, an ignorant army undone; a benediction on you for the joy you gave. I lie upon your eyelids light as light; we two shall gain again. (The further I withdraw, the deeper private trench I fortify, defensive, the more I come to recognize how banal a story this is, what fingernail parings we one and all leave. Soot from a brush fire speckles the page; what are we but analogies to Everyman's morning, dark night? From any residual distance, see, we still do conform to the ancestral mold—clay pigeon following pigeon; shoot out our eyes and you get a whore's shoe. That this is the coldest progression, I know: man loses wife to the oldest profession, luck, life. Mere repetition of the myth with no beginning grandeur—Astrid's lame left ankle stands as emblem of the snake.) I do remember sleeping on a

46

horsehair mattress once, fugitive from dying, huddled in a crazy
quilt, beneath a canopy, the four oak posters tapering to crown
my pillowed head, in Salem, Massachusetts, where the ghosts
still singe and flame, an ancient house maintained by the
historical society, each detail embalmed, accurate to the point
of no plumbing, caretaken by my friend, its two-hundred-year
dead first owner a trader in opium, slaves, and in the stables a
carriage stood waiting, erect by my bed waited bed warmer,
pan, upon the walls hung baleful captains, in the closet, gingham, fur; I heard the wind unfasten doors and climb the stairs
in shoes; I slept a fitful, haunted sleep, wakened to see every
candle alight, the snow blown thick outside, and yet I would
so quickly give this night for that, this past night mastered but
only with cognac, and then only just, and each floor board
creaking I hoped would be you—or gladly iterate all childhood
horror, and every sickbed sweated through I would embrace
instead of health—for this is past all bearing, cannot be re-
borne. (The difficult descent to reconciliation worked until I
thought again that you had never spoken to me of those shadows, stood immobile, would not qualify the past with present
gratitude. Head bent, retracting the distance just traveled,
retracing the mortality of marriage—as what mountain climber,
strung to a taut rope, his partner's mistake, has not felt his
fingers conform to a knife, the instant of pure instinct, desiring
release—exhausted, above all, with recurrence, stopped, I
stood and looked at you, named the game not worth the candle,
left Marseilles and luggage at the pier.) Huysmans said that,
after twenty, words alone suffice—an idea holds no further
interest. Abstraction of your body has induced this incoherence,
introduced distraction, is a thought. It is in the winter we see
breath congeal, have accurate vision of speech. (Canceled,
canceled, each divot replaced, all vestige of sport turned awry,

the name of action lost, a current dried to trickle, pith poured
to sap, string snapped, currant jellied and pitless, pitiless, paste,
I lie a blotted line. Bloated, blurred, the letters spread to echo,
a Marabar-marred mirror misaddressed—my message grows
inaccurate and characters go dim. Dew Drop Inn. Sans Souci.
Having a Wound-Awful Time. Help ululate; hell, pullulate;
respond sloughs off to despond, reap to deep. The graylag
geese above us have receded in formation; for your information
I still hunger, honk, a vanishing V, vague ague. The litter of a
litoral, a literal letter, is weed.) Black cats hunt goldfish from
the wall, spear, crunch, fastidious; oleander hides them where
they feed. We have the largest water basin for twelve miles.
"No wonder she left him," they say. Again, this desertion, wild
words all escaped—it soon shall be evening, your favorite time.
(False crocodile on either arm, face immersed in watermelons,
foot encumbered with papaya, Anthony Anderson sat. He collected synonyms for the one verb impose, reached twenty,
added slang. Red, black ants were tendrils on the white hair
of his calf; apathetic, Anthony read Crabbe, Roget and Fowler,
Burke.) To be no more than shadow, insubstantial, faded, page
in a pageant, transformed; to be not always the one son noticed,
the sore thumb stuck—if I might I would delight in habit,
orders, veil, would tear myself out of this vale. Like grass,
subdued, I should shed all imprint, grow pasture on the past,
cast off these widower weeds. To be no more than mourning
come to consciousness, a flower unfolding in sun, to not be
becoming but just be becalmed; if plausible, possible, I surely
would—as if, in this stomach-pumping, vastation, I could.
In all he said and did a perfect gentleman, enamored of
exorbitance, the swearwords singing in his head like larks,
ascetic (Man is nature questioning God, said Goethe, who
thought God was nature but loved to pronounce and repeat),

48

my friend Mondan hopscotched through bars and was the cat of nine tails, ever ready, well breaded, ardent, sliced by a scalpel to peace. (Blowfish balloon here like faith. At night, sometimes, still, I think it more than the wind at my door, that the squirrels thumping tile are you, and sometimes, still, believe. Dreams of disloyalty—the philter filtered out—recur; you found my door locked, shut. How could I in such order lose the one prize won, the single laurel worn? Honor drowns face down, knees up; the name of this fish is *à bas*.) In the shaken, swaying upper crook of a bare cherry tree, while nearby jays pecked, hovered, and flew chattering in wrath, with still a silver paper flag protruding from plucked branches, I, athwart the topmost bending bough with face upturned to air, remembered then our introduction—the twenty-fourth year *de mon âge*. In Cambridge, at a graceless party, wandering outside, I heard you singing from the center of an elm, climbed to find you poised there, twenty feet in sky, and while the others sought us and their noise arose, withdrew, we sat in moonlight, meeting, the leaves live beneath your feet. *Mi ritrovai per una selva oscura, Che la diritta via era smaritta.* Now birds have, circling, slaughtered the outlaw jay. (Hilary Eglinton languished at Leeds, ate only artichoke soup. Obsessed with tweeds and hound's-tooth checks, cricketer predicting locusts, manicured and monocled, his Pimm's Cup overflowing, his relatives distraught, Hilary, a lepidopterist, threatened his terrier with nets, diagnosed mass leprosy, diagramed the Loch Ness monster, sailed to the Isle of Wight.) Most of all, as I caper, cartwheel, prance, I consider heritage and what my father left. Is it some childhood guilt that I here expiate, a retroaction for some audience unkindness—telling him I knew his jokes—infant cruelty? Do I play the fool as he did; do I court defeat because he once was vanquished; have I at length followed suit? My shoes are large enough to track

49

those footsteps now, and my distraction forms, perhaps, his peace. He was a sunshine man, however, ringed around with favor, partiality—there never could have been an audience unkindness; with all his slips supported, no single fall stayed fell. To hold some slight inheritance of that bright aureole, to be beloved as by all he altogether was, to have my poor performance praised and each mishap applauded—to have my imitation forge equivalent respect is the deep purpose of this pilgrimage, and stands his lasting legacy, my shame. (How shall a man name sons? You should have had children hanging like grapes; I chew on our past like a cow. I cuddle it cudlike at night—the old familiar troubles; mature manure. What kept you barren, bare? My provident self insufficient at service; refrain.) Great god in any other guise was the result of Hera; what woman could have gainsaid Zeus, had he but appeared as himself? The bull, bird, wanderer are getups contrived to help get away, bereft of lordliness, his strong self lost, altered, antlered, godhead hid, to lull a jealous wife. Just so, diminished, disguised, I tread this earth a beast, lately walk up and down. The light, infrequent ferries to our village battled wind. With a clanking of chains (carry on), one searchlight missing buoys, the captain guzzling beer, carrion for Charon, inglorious cargo to cross, the foghorn a whistle, a wheeze, the white lights of dock a green daisy before us, the pitch of the sea a slow curve —intrepid, we swung and struck out. (This is the anniversary of Dante, Yeats, of Fitch. Rummy Fitch rum-ran from Martinique to Charleston, oarsman on a log—tied a note to his neck and lay down. The note, water-soaked, shredded, read: "For the love of Jesus, put me in a bottle, please, and I shall rest content. Float for the price of a bob." May gulls whitewash you gently, my hero, master, corpse. What error everywhere: Fitch marinated in drink. I am most sober, somber, calm, a lake at bay, lagoon. Let us return to Grasse: the vendors sold sweet chocolate where Fragonard once sketched. The rose girls hawked their perfumed selves, daubed dry behind the ear. I munched a rind of goat's cheese, sang: "Sweet summer, leave us not"—until, little chicken, sky fell.) This city's miserable minions cannot but oppress me now; a bit of indiscriminate love and lice are in my long locks too, a three-day stubble on this chin, a Panama bandless hat; I also have been yes your waterfront walker, your street sleeper, fool, have poised upon your driven piles and thought of an oil slick on skin; I equally have wintered with a ten-cent drink of wine, have chased newspaper for the wad and lifted cans for loot, blear-eyed, beer-leer-eyed I have seen the dawn come up like dawn, have timpanied upon the tin-topped garbage of your park, have cowered at the mangy cats and torn tar from my toe; I too, I too have heard the crazed men mutter that this life must change. (Festivity ended, the word cycle closed, I am again begun. Dancers on the shore retreat; our revelry is revery and each pipe, hoof grows dim. Initiates do not eat meat; I am weary of innards and tripe. Deeper than did ever plummet sound lies silence, echo and release.) With the coming of sunset the olive trees folded, mothers suckling, wreathed to themselves, and down the valley's length the first night lights came visible, glasses raised from hill to hill in illumined salutation, pharos to this other Egypt, shutters expectant of storm or fastened expectant of moths and mosquitoes; there in April we would walk through windless crescive dusk, diagraming early stars and gathering anemones (Astrid wrapped in her white cloak could dispossess the climbing moon and crickets scare to silence, frozen in their farandole), purple flower faces cradled in your hand, and purple tipped the high pine tops while Cannes showed forth its violet nimbus, neon blanket far

51

below—and in the city plain women wept, their lot to be but pillars in that roofless temple, flesh. Gone to her long last home is love, defaced with inauspicious scars, our monument dilapidated, water at a severed neck (on All Soul's Day Rimbaud did say: "*Je t'envoie à l'enfer*") each fitful dream unreal and dampened, wish washed with the breaking ice, immolated maidens pinioned on a russet sky, the jagged lightning, tender thunder, rain submersed in, merged with darkness (watch that man bend eight feet down, unstrap his harnessed shoe and rub, his crutches teetering, the sad soft head and shoulders humped; round the pituitary like a pea his carcass burgeons, burdened—something like a toe emerges, flesh, and then my separated uncle, torn, killed upon the intersection of Bombay and Papenburg) and, I am reminded, in this reign of absence, as from every other refuge, all of us is gone. I have a surfeit, a sufficiency of words; lamely let us order halt, stop, staunch. Flow gently, sweet Often—still, silt, cease. Pry off thy madcap, jester, rest; we hold no more taste for this caper; attempt, for once, the tale. Astrid has gone away, with Triapin, from France—not with him, but on his account, and to her family. I prithee, jury, judge; as I now find it difficult just to transmit the story, as husband I could never tell her, simply, stay my wife. A mythopoetic manhandler of joy, panhandling the gift I had gaffed: dumb bum. This distraction has left me distracted; ham in the stir, hamster in cage, whither would'st wend, for rest, for trees?—an elf among the elms. When engaged in lake-locked coitus, however, it is preferable, surely, to keep the partner's head above water. Thus sayeth our lewd—or give her artificial respiration; don't pollute the drink. I am, Astrid, beleaguered by want, and I await you still. Who tastes of your *sauce chaloise*, steak; who swallows your strawberry mousse? Ephemerid, thy name is love, and, scarab, thine is lust. Why post with such hot haste, and never write at all? The acorns drop like mail upon the garden table, bounce; you have been too precipitate, unkind. *Apollon hat mich geschlagen,* cried Hölderlin, incensed, but then, in his cell, grew direct: I am a demi-Tasso served *mit schlag.* Not wholly devoid of invention, perhaps, but altogether devious, intention in a maze. Amassed, my coin might once have held value (heed golden Ariadne's threat, "Thees ees a thread, a lead"); melted talents are brass. Pirated doubloons can't double, currency runs out, and you refused to wait. I, languishing in language, maintain as yet vestigial pride; I shall not answer your silence with letters, am driven to work as escape. This is the quest in question, the prose in praise of filly; parch the valley pale, sir king, fish for your own gruel. I am appalled with waste, the telltale untouched crumb, while six million monthly must go undernourished, and the ripe, rotted peach. One glove should shroud one hand. Accept the gaunt, let hindrance, dare. And consciously, I tell you, for I am no fool (each academic honor hangs upon my wall; I was a terrible infant, big-headed, argumentative, debating with the elders), this romantic *roman* shall solace, splice himself on sword. From ritual residual; a printer's devil, slugged, is mightier than pen. I leave you a villainous testament, being of sound mind and bawdy. This bad lad of dames of tempo past fast. Tempt us; *fugit;* the last page is the last. A separate treaty, private dance; Horatio; deign not to be a Dane. Air sings beneath my feet and mauls the metatarsals in garroted gavotte. I, witnessed, will you peace. *Ja dis.* Hermetically sealed, a vacuum-packed tongue, abhorrent to nature (so easy to sing, chorus, sign: Jack and Jill looked up the frill to fetch a pill for what ails her—pudding and souse, thumb in an eye, mud in a pie, horn her in corner, plumb tuckered puckered pukka'd out, a lecherous treacherous

Villon)—see how rhyming simplifies the thought and carries to its own conclusion circular inanity. In my end is my beginning, mulberry bush and bird. (Poetasters, prurient, luxuriant-locked, preen, pose. Green grows the greengage in my lady's cage; lilacs in hedgerows are now all the rage. Protogonos, protagonist, ordained the Crab and Archer, nailed this black sky fabric with white twinkling carpet tacks. Your short left leg goes dancing on my mitral valve and lung. Instead of Troy shall lip-sucked soul be sacked. What gnu conjunction, wilde-beest, beset Concepta there? Unintelligible utterances mut-tered at the mud; my ventricle remembers how you used to lean and limp.) VACANCY, the sign asserts, and so we are assigned. I am finished with punning, protestation, assignation, rites; the party, pray, is over now, the dappled steeds too hoarse to neigh, the players harried home. (A loon flaps heavily and calls across the recollected lake that lay behind our hut; be-neath the water, clicked rooks carry with no loss of sound. Shore is bordered with refusals and refuse; none but the sub-merged can hear that coded signal, tide.) Still, from this final distance, my sundered sunlit body followed by no single shade, the tall grass flat beneath my feet and smoke a leafless tree in air, still, pierced by memory like butterfly to paper, wingless, pinned to pain—the litter of a carnival is silence after noise, sterility and loss; within this grave and emptied field I only hear echoed—that long last cry and falling sound, the sever-ance, the parting, teeth bared, then hidden, darkened, torn, lips shaped to cry the form once felt (as once a traveler, the dust washed from cloth sandals and rope sack renewed with bread, bent-kneed to thank his once-seen host, or young son sent to war, old woman worn with severance has grieved and said and heard that newly full-filled word): you turning said farewell.

2

THE
DISMEMBERED
DIONYSUS

The one gold thread of my few fool's strands: notes toward a supreme faction. . . . There is a Salmon of Wisdom; eat of its flesh and know all. The Salmon you cooked us this evening, I gained an Eztra Pound. . . . The tilapia fish, when digested by the leprous, leaves but a leper to live. . . . Is there no distinction, ever, between that which one was and that which one wishes to be? . . . *"Partir, c'est courir un peu."* . . . Shan't we chant *oui?* . . . A jawbone like chicken fat, wish I'd said that. . . . Astrid, Astrid, Astrid. . . . In the Taiping Rebellion, when twenty million died, they fought because of railroad lines, crisscrossing China, barbarian wires that rusted with rain. Hung, the office seeker, screamed that wires impaled the good low-flying spirits, that red rusting drops were their blood. Twenty million died to save the dead. . . . My love wearing roses; were a bird to see you, he would think it spring. . . . Alexander held raw food in front of his griffins, then, emperor, flew at the sun. . . . Bocephalus Bridled, a possible title? . . . Only when their wings were singed did chariots return. . . . The sweet infested stream; consider faith. . . . Nine worthies once took peacock vows; I crossed the fleet at Barfleur; crass Crécy bowed submission, and still eye sweeps the field. . . . Pull your-

self together is seldom said to those who can. . . . This
morning at the olive press, a man collapsed, rose, fell.
. . . The little fish, Jhasa, grown great, saved Manu
(who protected it when young) from flood. . . . Fidelity,
said Baudelaire, is one of the signs of genius. But
think of Jeanne Duval. . . . God walks in mysterious
ways. Neither delighteth he in any man's legs. Astrid,
I delighteth in yours. . . . Where is the yeast of yester-
year, and whither tomorrow's tart? . . . Better to lie
together than tell the truth apart. . . . I want each
budding flower nipped. . . . The sky above belies the
mud below, old belle dame this earth; beldam cry mercy,
lift high the faint susurrous skirt of your subjective
praise: the omnipotent raineth, ages and ague. . . .
Cheerful are the labors of the loon. . . . Alchemy increases the spiritual content of lead. . . . So what I
speak is just. . . . Indra freed the waters. . . . Nothing
will come between Astrid and me; from a half-
understood, defensive platitude, that became certain.
. . . I think it was Homer who said: She was a nice
girl in respect of size, shape, diaphragm, and house-
work. . . . What chagrinnning at? . . . Merlin laughed
three times: once at a seeming-virtuous queen he knew
to keep a lover, once at a beggar whose dung heap held
treasure, and once at a small boy carrying shoes that
Merlin knew he would not live to wear. . . . A beautiful man with hay in his seed, the new mutant, eating
desert for forty years, embroidering cacti on tin. . . .
For joie thai wepe with her eize, that hem so sounde
ycomen seize. Now king Orfeo newe coround is, and
his quen dame Heurodis. . . . A kind of stupid insistence on the obvious that can generate power foreign
to subtlety. . . . *Adikia* is sinfulness and stifles the
divine. . . . In my draft and swollen art, the soul of

wit is levity and ladies were deceivers ever, living off
the fat of other people's land, one foot on the sore.
. . . That vague vogue started, grew, and Triapin hung
ten; at the crest of each wave he surfaced, twiddling
mustachios, negligent, siren-sung, rich. . . . Sovereign
artifice subsides; come celebrate the real. . . . Celebrate
again the dying of the wight, against the sickened fere.
. . . Ask for a prophylactic, and it shall be given; de-
mand a contraceptive, and receive a stare. . . . In that
Catholic country, despair. . . . We keep returning to
the berth, the hotel bed and not the Bible used as
pillow, girl spread giddily on Gideon, the tablets swallowed and not followed, giltly turning radio, control.
. . . Christ asked for wine, not vinegar; they gave him
this, the lees. . . . To lessen ease, a lesson: "I thirst,
I thirst," he cried. . . . I also, a sponger, expunge. . . .
Why were you way late; were you on the waylaid? . . .
A dragonfly flits past me; my cup runneth ever anon.
. . . Anonymous Bosch. . . . Go pipe within an ivy
leaf; providence provides. . . . *Tel qui. rit vendredi
dimanche pleurera.* . . . He who laughs last laughs,
the beast. . . . Valkyrie *vendredi, dimanche* Valhalla.
. . . We had an argument one morning, absurd, about
books—how they should stand on the shelf. . . . I
wanted them straight, she in stacks. . . . She and her
lazy majesty and me; a stellar constellation. . . . With
art one can create, with women procreate. . . . Astrid,
eye delighteth in yours. . . . Capitulation is ever preferable to recapitulation; why should I write here, lorn
loon? . . . Love holds the sea in its place, said Boethius,
his great music box, the organized sky. . . . Small comfort and no consolation; I'll rant as well as he. . . .
Cupide, oute of alle charitee; go take a few falls with
my god. . . . My god but I am sad, am sod, to meet

you on the *matt,* as we Germans would say; I would
as meet mete meat. . . . A pearl among white peas. . . .
Oysters there are as big as an elbow. . . . Astrid. . . .
The familiar mutation of thought; how what is past
grows poignant, and what is present, dull. . . . What's
happening, what's happened, what. . . . Become he
whom you are. . . . W*erde,* verdant Werther, dubious
at best. . . . Out of my *Michelin,* this: Provençal Person-
alities. Fragonard (1732–1806). Painter, born at Grasse.
Hard worker with a lackadaisical manner. Thiers (1797–
1887). Statesman and historian, born at Marseilles.
Taste for politics. . . . Lug was red, the color of the
setting sun, from sunset to sunrise. . . . This excellent
o'erhanging canopy; I stand here yawning; it's an awn-
ing. . . . Panic is the fear engendered by the great god
Pan. . . . One prays to heaven, hopes to hell. . . . A
dusty fiddle is better than none at all. Laity triumphant.
. . . Still, there is still Astrid. . . . A dewdrop tree hangs
stars from its branches; its roots protect the world. Two
wolves chase light across the sky, and, on the final day,
they shall devour all. . . . The dead pass over that thin
Bridge of Hair; they must not fall below. . . . (Or
spaced around the house, by shutters, in books, at the
ant trap, your notes: "Thanks for the food and drink.
And things." "Listen. Everywhere I love you." "Mother
Hubbard shops." "You may now write me a letter.
Because you can type." "Can I sew? How well?" I look
at them and laugh.) . . . Out of these sundered elements we reconstruct an entity. . . . Actinium, Ruthen-
ium, Palladium, Titanium, Zirconium. . . . Oway, what
ther was wepe and wo, when he, that hadde ben king
with crown, went so poverlich out of town! . . . Trust-
ing, he went from the throne down to die. . . . And
in the sixth generation sing peace. . . . Kore submitted

60

to both of the brothers, hurled without end, chthonic, rolled. . . . Cotys and Bendis, thy Thracians thrash, thresh. . . . He com into a fair cuntray . . . Araucanian Indians nicely distinguish the small shades of hunger, cut offal off their dead. . . . Knee, heel, knee see, bone, um. . . . When the turtle turns, trees shake; the mammoth stable mirror stands appreciative witness of that well-dressed lonely lady who constructed it, paraded there, matching her habit and horse. . . . Oysters and egrets, herons and moss, one old bull endure. . . . In 1823, the firm of Figrench and Herlade bought sixteen million feet of long-leaf timber, pine; sawdust piles remain. . . . Not as a complication resolved, but as a situation revealed. . . . A certain calm that argued order. . . . Cassiopeia, head held down, learns humility. . . . Remember the white Coleman light by my tent. . . . *Quondam futuris*, sent y meant. . . . A single gull and helicopter share the nighttime sky. . . . This, the meaningless concretion. . . . Niched is ever man. . . . Chance meetings, purest chance; think what would have happened had Actaeon met Aphrodite and not Artemis. . . . It is impossible to approach tragedy from more than one point of view, improbable to look at comedy from one vantage alone. . . . A setback induces tenderness. . . . Fluke like a bad dream of Blake. . . . What can be more loveless than emperor and eunuch, Triapin and I? . . . The pupil and the apple of his sty, glazed glaze. . . . Fine me an honest man to slake my every slackening, toe line. . . . We pirouette, piranha, attendant on the upturned throat, the raised glass, half-shut lid. . . . All teeth and lost conviction; worse, intensity. . . . Nor never shall such passion know again. . . . Blaze, blaze, the fire of counterfeit—virtue entered into virtuosity—this pyre of gold sold to fools. . . .

Brave men the last wave buy. . . . Drowned Palinurus'
kelplike hands bless sharks with each shock, ripple,
strike, indulgent until they are wrist. . . . Polyneices,
vulture feast, festers where he fell; bees nest within his
thigh. . . . Hero plumbs the Hellespont; another man
done gone. . . . Visible from Scheidegg, pitonned to
the sheer cliff fall, a stalactite of bone, a body weathers
winter—and snow is snow, ice, ice. . . . Voyager, attend;
tentative, pitch tent. . . . This world is not your world
nor life your life. . . . We crawl to stand to stoop; our
shadows shift in sun; a time to reap, a time to weep;
show me the color of his eyes. . . . Poetry is christen-
ing and burial at once; what better epigraph than this
as epitaph? . . . Abishag the Shunammite lay in David's
bed, and he knew her not. . . . Say; a funny thing happened on the way to work—(our savory savior who with,
eyes sore?)—not altogether disagreeable, said the lady
to the soldier; when will you solder, when plumb? . . .
I refuse to ascribe this effect to that cause; there is no
reason, finally, but incident, accident, waste. . . . What
happens after our brief paragraph, parenthesis of breath
—post-crypt? . . . A sudden, strange belief in nobility;
to care a little more than strictly requisite; the possible
heroic way to live. . . . The old king lay unwarmed,
his harp unheard and with Absalom hung . . . Canadel
. . . Entrevaux . . . Falicon. . . . The deaf are deft;
Astrid will leave next week. . . . Why call it lunacy;
the sun has addled marginalia, has scrambled brains
as egg. . . . My Lorelei, my siren, myrrh maid, human
voices waking us sing mi—*Far la sot idiot*. . . . Secure
yourself with rope; it is a swan-sin song. . . . The fog
creeps, little cat; I have been ganched in haunches by
a crashing boar. . . . Digging a new ditch, underneath
the green fig tree, I shaped it as our bathtub, sat spread

on the earth to assume your positions, saw between my disjunct thighs a sardine, razor, bone. . . . Even my garbage, my "*trou*" so preceded, the dry ground passed water, my spade has been spayed. . . . That waste is not original, nor sewage newly pipes, that the disemboweled, the recent prostrated castrated, wait turns—that the dry ground has been pre-turned I learned. . . . The daughter goeth down; the son cometh up. . . . Margins miss, the Medean grows average, light goes full circle; vanity, concentric, starts anew. . . . Greetings in a bottle, bobbing bobbin, corked (labeled ale, the hare of the dog, bravest boat, good for what ails you, country of the young), we have naked drunk deep from thee, sea. . . . Post coitum, Aristotle, I am every animal, *bouteille triste*, trussed, spent, sane. (*La mere amère me dit maudit*; Thetis binds bone with salt anemones; to wield a strident trident, foam. . . . I have climbed the yew tree, made it bow.) Why call it lunacy; the sun has addled *oeufs au plot*. . . . Thus com Sir Orfeo out of his care, God grant ous alle wele to fare. . . . When the famous jeweler died, his daughter wore a black bikini. . . . Pent-angles form an endless knot, tough nut to crack, hang many a tar-oh, burden man's pack. . . . The devil is old; grow old to understand. . . . At new moon (this is augury), the sea birds that ride the ninth wave from the shore are the souls of the dead. . . . Must one always turn the irrational into a moral imperative? . . . Think of the cigarettes bought at Entraunes; she broke the wrapper with her nail and turned to kiss me twice. . . . Why begin a story with "Everyone knows the story of"?—or why, thus begun, continue? . . . These more or less elaborate fictions called fiction. . . . Proverb: Indecision is like the stepchild. If he doesn't wash his hands he's called dirty;

if he does, he is wasting the water. . . . I believe the most powerful mood and emotion for me is that of renunciation, of impending loss acknowledged, or possibility denied. . . . Astrid embraces the diarrheality. . . . That woman's hair bends instead of curls. . . . Madcaps are what the jesters wore. . . . King Arthur must have a miracle before he sits to dinner. . . . In Vermont, driving, I saw a misspelled sign: Outhouse Orchids, it read. Gory be to God on the Cross. There is still Tim. . . . George III, when riding in Windsor Park with his queen, approached a venerable oak and shook a branch with the utmost cordiality and regard. . . . Converging to converse. . . . Rishyacringa in the forest caused the rain to fall. The *sihtu* plants grew not. . . . Never let the pond run to sea when spats split. . . . Thug; thaga. . . . The name Sirenia was accorded sea cows (manatees) because, when seen from afar, particularly with a baby under the flipper, they were thought to be mermaids. These aquatic mammals have a torpedo-shaped body that ends in a horizontal fluke. Order Sirenia. . . . But is that also why they were called Man-tease? . . . Put yourself in ordure. . . . Does education pay off? You bet it does. Because the more you learn, the more you earn. . . . A girl wearing green is jaded, wearing yellow, jaundiced. . . . This, from Tolstoy: "I called it a quarrel, but it was not really a quarrel; it was only the discovery of the gulf which was in reality between us." . . . The apostolic posture peters, palls; I do not wish to curry lions, scurry into catacomb; thy pagan cruelty exacted full submission—and it is enacted, I submit. . . . The light, infrequent fairies in our village bottled wind, plunked, plucked the Aeolian harp. . . . A cord tied round yon burlap bag will steer you safely home. . . . We gambol through the gilt-edged fields, frisk, lambs. . . . Twinkle-toes was a black sheep and everybody knows—how he could flesh, could fleece you in twenty-three seconds, release: homosexuality is a cul-de-sac. . . . Neither do I find the goats enticing (here comes the bridle), nor swans. . . . Sicklied o'er with the appalling cost of thought, the paling plaster cast about my broken leg, axed pole, I am a conscience coward, still reserved, possessed. . . . A cord tied round yon tube will force shut all Fallopians open, will serve to cure, secure. . . . The best is never to be born (so take precautions), the next to sink unschooled. . . . Tutored into fluency, puckered Puck, I am an iceberg upside down, nine-tenths above the surface, cold, top-heavy, ludicrous: Titania with her Bottom raised, skirts furled to the moon. . . . O bear on, Oberon, the aisle is full of noise. . . . That life may be beginning and not a long sad end cannot come clear to me; alms and the mien I sing on such a night as this. . . . Dido of the wild she flanks shall drink her wine to moonshine bright; light is commencement, quartered, all shall start anew. . . . And yet I cannot choose but weep to seem so disarrayed, red petals plucked, green stem unstuck, blue flower of the pasture past. . . . Unhappily deceased, of a long illness, of a brief illness, suddenly, we fold our morning papers to the final page. . . . Art thou not sick of silly puns, poor structure, camouflage? I lie beneath this tent of sky and wish to share in sleep. . . . The one thing that you hid from me is all I picture yet, your sleep, as now your public, new-found self stands foreign, awakened, unreal. . . . Astrid, I shall drink champagne from some glass slipper soon; I will not waste away like this, my kingdom in unrest. . . . Like that poor fool the moon I shall grow great to fade. . . .

65   The people have admonished me: I do not smile, pa-

rading; a delegation of serfs sent fruit to pray each
health was high. . . . I peeled a peach, disdainful, could
not grin. . . . Kane-milo-hai found Lo-hi-au's spirit as
a single water bird. . . . Upon what wave crest will I
soar, which future shore inhabit, where, flocking, find
new ground? . . . Amazons cut off a breast in order
to pursue the chase; what disfigurement will not the
chaste accept when once they quarry, hunt? . . . Philoctetes, the smell of such artists is murdering Paris;
Oenone repents too late. . . . A good king wenches,
lass; look out. . . . We argue occupation by a day re-
plete with trivia, laze the nighttime hours so we may
resume, presume. . . . It was the foremost angel that was
tempted to produce the show, then fell, fired instead.
. . . Five smiles a simile, a mile. . . . I am grown muddle-
headed, mazy motion Me(le)andering. . . . The Sibyl,
raving, utters unadorned, unlovely words, but is the
thousand-year-old godhead's voice. . . . Whider thou
gost, ichil with the, and whider y go, thou schalt with
me. . . . (As a man fillets fish, Marduk split the body
of Tiamat. . . . Loki, transformed, was the hag Thokk;
the hag Thokk was a crow. . . . "The way she puts
down speed cops going up the strip—and fucky-knuckles
Ferdie, that's our boy." . . . "Visit this tailor and have
six suits made, at my expense, of course; come with
me to Guatemala where the nights are long. Touch
upon the soft seashore in this my aquaplane. . . . You
shall couple with her as do locomotives, be my sole
son and one heir. My daughter, star, sand, air"—Cavil-
laca sat beneath the lucma tree.) . . . The name of the
bow there is life. . . . Thou, Aristide, beekeeper, watch
the hive and wive. . . . I feel my poor craft ebbing, my
freude no more *jung*. . . . Beware; mad digs; buy, weir,
wear stakes, keepsakes, keep off the keep, key inhibits

this habitation, *qui*, habit, ha' pity, I have thee key, *qui sache*, sash, *qui sait*, say, forgive us our trespass. . . . Fixed, frozen, ill-hinged, split—never was Seder sadder, nor the chair so empty; Judas trees reached bloom. . . . We ate at La Reserve, a restaurant that once was chapel, walled with four-foot pitted stone. . . . Is it the Dead Sea I must cross to get to campground, Jordan, sir? And will you bomb my potash plant if I bring back the brine? . . . Like glist'ring Phaeton, however (descendant from what was ascendant, wanting the manage of unruly Hades), we are o'erthrown—yet now in throes I labor, toss, spray sheets about me as the sea, am grave. . . . Why did the chicken cross the road? Why, that was no chicken, that was my life. . . . Who was that piccolo I saw you with? That was no oboe, that was my fife. . . . Hecate completes the empty angling net. . . . The street lights throughout Madison went yellow when we met. . . . In somer he liveth bi wild fruit, and berren bot gode lite; in winter may he nothing finde bot rote, grasses and the rinde. . . . Thor cast for the Midgard snake and Yahwe for leviathan; Christ is a fisher of men. . . . Walled Troy: no stallion ever rutted mare than this; no hectoring fool shall get foal. . . . It will be a hard winter; I shall pillage, shear, and burn. . . . We do Chinese Hand. . . . Please Used Other Door. . . . A man scraped at the sidewalk with his spade, announced he would grow turnips in cement. . . . "Be he, missy, your house-bound?" . . . Euchred into euchymy; seeming, however, euchroite. . . . Notebook, not (eh) book. . . . Herod, he married this nice Jewish girl, and you should see her daughter dance. . . . Last week, invited by the baroness, before she left, for tea—she, cautious, polite, draped in cats, debating Palestrina, not questioning my quartered self, drawn up on elbows, balanced—while I lusted, longed for the reputed, therapeutic drink, we chatted, chid. . . . Silence is inaccurate; the mistral, banshee, blew. . . . I sat suspended, lion-loined, a saturated particle, poised in poison, posed, molecular, kite-high. . . . (Sodden, rather; why write I was suddenly drunk if untrue? There issued no glimmer of glamour from this falling star, mediorite.) . . . She pored, bored, poured. . . . Insoluble, a potent potion portentous of headache, Do Tell. . . . Seven thousand jasmine blossoms weigh a kilo, merely, and the peasant women pick. . . . Overturned trucks on the road to Jerusalem testify to Arab-held hills once, to war. . . . Hung like a wreath athwart the transmission, I lie a dried memorial to each drive shaft exploded, a poor progression ambushed, cascaded, a proud conned convoy gone. . . . Ready when you are, C.G. . . . *Ci-gît.* . . . No mawkish monk nor murderer can stand so close-confined; I wonder if you truly know what isolation means. . . . This cell. . . . Tonight, hunched, muttering, I know our anniversary and pray that you are girdled, girded, spread upon no other bed. . . . Relentless, barren, bearing like the baroness a sugar lump to sweeten age, we can but face a future less alarum, with no belle. . . . The bawdy second hand of time ticks on the point of five. . . . Fie, fie, a rooster roisters, henna-haired, curry-combed, cluck-cluck. . . . Angelic, when I had thundered in, she, having thumped the floor as summons, opened her right eye to wink. She hid beneath the sheets, pretended sleep, three pillows over her head, protesting noise, or hid behind the door, absurdly dressed, a hide to seek, my love. I shook her till she shook. . . . Three minutes have passed and the second church chimes; stuccoed, the bell tower rises spotlit, and I alone am exited, blown as a leaf to Africa   68

and braced beneath our single sky. . . . Orion also
thine. . . . Happy Anniversary. . . . To the glorious
dead, salve, unction, sleep. . . . In my twenty-eighth
year, a water-wrecked deck, covered in coral: stay well.
. . . Jubilation T. Early; a wait. . . . Rip-a-titian and
you have a Tint-a-rent-oh; waley, waley, down the brae;
we maun stop maundering, however, feel somehow at
peace. . . . Lack of control is both means and an end;
heraldic, maleficent, gentle, we organize paper and
press. . . . Gronw and Blodeuwedd usurped the dominion of Lleu. Lleu became an eagle, she, an owl, but
by his subject's wand he was restored. She, hateful in
the eyes of birds, lives still. . . . Turmeric, a rhizome
spice, perennial, flavors mustard, curry powder, and my
mouth. . . . Astrid: a fierce old man upon a donkey
greeted me; I bowed. Patriarchal hand twitched to rein
—upon the incline of the road I bent my back, sup-
pliant. . . . Here, with bread, cheese, wine, I am returned, was gone. . . . You did not know black olives
from the dried sheep dung. . . . Things fall altogether
apart; the scent air cannot hold. . . . I have of late
oblated and been blessed. . . . We neither rise nor sleep
with sun, yet petulant nighttime petals shed. We are so
lino-typical, correctly keyed in space. . . . Minos, king
of Crete, laid siege to Megara. . . . Apollo killed Orion
though a goddess bent the bow. . . . Dog his footsteps,
dog, until black night is day. . . . Children cry for
Argus and his record of devotion, final wag. . . . Pryderi
brided Kicva, the daughter of Gwynn Gloy. . . . A
mistral commences to blow. . . . The renting pain of
re-enactment, a worn-out poetical stud. . . . So here
I am, ejaculating graffiti, elliptical, arcane. . . . Outside,
irises die and stink; inside, the fleur-de-lis lie, swink.
69   . . . For the assumption of presumption, Thamyris lost

sight and Marsyas was flayed alive. . . . Ahab died in hemp. . . . Honor, previous to Clarimunda, was the single mistress of Huon. . . . How exceeding strong is wine; temper it with music; thy sweet name alone. . . . I yet presume to subsume in ourself our selves. . . . Oh, that my words were written, that we might wrest rest. . . . From a foolish, grape-guzzling baby, he is born a cyclic god; in his blessed recurrence, we perceive the growth of fruit. . . . Myopic, in his tinted lens, high-pitched, owl-eyed, false, the rolls of fat above his belt embellished with a vine leaf, fig. . . . Proteus taught Aristaeus true repentance, constancy, the chains of fire, flood, release. . . . What imitative cosmic egg did Leda lay that we know not? . . . In Elizabeth, N.J., the husbands roll for partners, wives (what the deuce, speak, dice, let the dough see dough). . . . Salt, selling at sixty cents a bushel in Nassau, bought, for the rebel blockade runners, one hundred dollars in turpentine along the Georgia coast—Do not dwell in Llewdness, neither live in Evil; God is love, god is vengeful, love is vengeful, jealous, good. . . . This cat abases; katabasis. . . . Absinthe makes the heart grow fonder. . . . I have to look forward to but looking back. . . . Abstinence makes the heart grow fodder. . . . Fame and frenzy, the needles click, chatter, track, give. . . . Papa likes his bourbon, mamma likes her gin; papa likes his bourbon, mamma likes her gin. . . . Give us, at least, the illusion of grace; give us, at last, reciprocal faith. . . . Papa likes his outside women, mamma likes her outside men. . . . Born beneath a sullen star, with suicide in full ascendance, vanished when the space within accepted space without. . . . This blistered membrane, flesh. . . . Papa likes his sherry, mamma likes her port; papa likes his sherry, mamma likes her port; papa likes

to shimmy, mamma likes to sport. . . . Anderson died
of a toothpick in Colon. . . . Default, dear Brutus, lies
not in our stars. . . . The well-planned impulse (draft
and lull) suggests: Think of Rimbaud's deathbed raving, Einstein's final unheard words; what a job to listen
to the whirlwind, what a loss in the translation; is it
not far calmer just to eye the storm? . . . *Necessite faict
gens mesprendre, E faim saillir le loup des boys.* . . .
Music is a young lung sung, a Chinese flute and trill.
. . . The parables of going and coming contained in
a pond, infatuated shellfish and the shelves of self. . . .
His rococo person flourished, florid, sank. . . . Art, they
say, is therapy, game, oracle, experiment; art as a necessity I understand perhaps. . . . A lifelong libertine in
pursuit of hippyness, snapping his fingers to song, the
"Ineluctable Modality Rag," Alexander chanted, seemed
a salad leaf sodden with oil. His watch was an alarm
clock also, buzzed for the birthdays of friends. . . . A
defrocked monk turned pederastic rabbinical student
clicks his heels in my mind's weightless corridor, upends
a book on kabbala before the bathroom, exits, excited
with mud. . . . Mist rises on the water basin; monks
once wore fish scales to demonstrate wisdom, clothe
in knowledge, godliness. . . . Crows sit on the chimney, then dive. . . . Mrs. Clapp ran an infirmary in Sarah
Lawrence, loved her girls not wisely and too well; burn
a diseased branch and you blight the nearby trees. . . .
The palm at the end of the hand. . . . Divination by
mirrors is catoptromancy, by a cock selecting grains,
alectryomancy, by wax thrown into water, ceromancy,
by salt, halomancy; divination by means of mice is
myomancy—unavailing all. . . . "I'll burn for thy sake,
Marjory, the town that thou liest in; an I'll mak the
baby fatherless, for I'll throw mysel therein." . . .

71

With ivory neck and pommels round and comely interval. . . . Amongst the faggots kindled with a chatting stick. . . . A smock is both a skirt and that which burns inside it, the deadly nightshade, bella donna; time after time we forget. . . . Mine is an ancient family and I its last degeneration; how I hoped for some bright babe to dandle, lap and knee. . . . Upon his head, her ringlets, rest nine hundred years of power; glory, lock, stock, barrel sunk to anonymity. . . . The fruit flies lie requited in this house. . . . Our house once hosted armies, furled an armada, gave alms. . . . I would have been so proud to press the coat of many colors carefully upon a son, to give and be continued, proud to take his arm. Or darling daughter dower with her beauty and the best: perfected and redeemed, all loss of integrity salved, each mortal coil unshuffled— I would have been so pleased. . . . What wanton god that plays with flies ordained me a ghost writer, last gasp and gas? . . . Ancestral echo-haunted, the old chap fallen, chip: just the desert, Sarah, ah, just deserts ahead. . . . One head of a family less, Ichabod, *Ich am boden*, abed abet, abide: hoarse man. . . . Papa-tu-a-nuku weeps beneath Rangi. . . . Tane-mahuta disjoined his parents, Earth and Sky. . . . Starfish recreate their separated selves; bound wounds need balm, need air. . . . We wage a losing battle with the light and have invented oil; we went "awhaling," widows walk. . . . Sandalwood is fire bark; Maui gave flame to men. . . . There's many a slip twixt the halter and altar. . . . *Wisse das Bild*. . . . Attar of roses bedizens thy cheek, whets the paper, scants not scent. . . . Death can come solicited within the street lamp's circle, stand between the hall and wall, hand on kilted hip. . . . Parallel we ski into infinity, knees taut in disconnection, ankles uninvolved. . . . We are deceived, disabused, wrung, wronged. . . . *Wolle die Wandlung.* . . . Change. . . . Just as Zeus has swallowed Metis, fathered then their joint conception, so we must, alone, bear Athena and wisdom once again. . . . Tattooed women, rigadooning, make their magic bellies bounce and watch the wind egg shiver, split, see the drunkards dance. . . . Adrasteia sits without the endless cave of Night. . . . Zeus became first, Zeus of the bright lightning last. . . . A torn blind beating in the wind, rain-struck, is our poor past. . . . Cardiac Classics. . . . Anatomy, Q. Mab. . . . The Yellowing Kid Ney. . . . (Hist.) Distended Heart. . . . He, that hadde ywed the fowe and griis and on bed the purperbiis, now on hard hethe he lith, with leves and grasse he him writh. . . . Dinner tonight at Le Chantecler, in a rainstorm, on a hill. . . . The valley lay tide-swept beneath us; the drowned lights of Grasse to the right. . . . Astrid ordered *entrecôte.* . . . A fat white rabbit slept beside us, two dogs beneath the table stalked a buttered shrimp; I practiced patois with the chef. . . . Astrid says that every meal she eats is the best meal ever eaten, and means it; every village seen is the most beautiful: I understood the rabbit more than her. . . . As people put on glasses in order to hear the better, just so do I write in order to wrong. . . . In this welter of inconsequence, honesty's confusion, whelmed detail coupling onto detail, the novelist talks to himself. . . . A public success concomitant with private fall is as old as the apposite story of Adam, bare as the winter hills. . . . Integrity is such an easy word but so indefinite; the sevenfold path is a sheep-pen sometimes, and fig leaves clothe ravening wolves. . . . I never had a lover who could eat crab apples, smile. . . . She street-walked, a withering, hithering nymph. Spawn spun inside of her as sprats; crustacea, catafalqued, merged into marrow, came limp out like lymph. Note, nodes; a bitter batter, but her. . . . Our false sensuality that is in fact fastidiousness, fine scents to cover smell. . . . *Niente*, thee, *dolce*, art far. . . . Life poses the conflict between love and truth; oh, but this vastation is vast. . . . With this ring I thee bed, yet would t'were wedtime and all well. . . . Stooping this morning to pick watercress, I saw my stretched face in the stream and was drunk. . . . We boats borne ceaselessly into the *piste*; I, Miss America. . . . If ever we grow glad again, I shall commemorate. . . . The harbor at Villefranche and Iles de Lérins. . . . That the water tastes foul, that Astrid decided to leave when the mice shredded pillows like wheat, shed fur like the antlers of elk (she, the piece that passeth understanding, our breakfast serial), six suicides fell from the former chateau—stands better left unsaid. . . . For all manner of thing shall be well. And all, even rheumy old ladies, all shall be well, shall stoop to pick pistols and stay men in droves. . . . Hope springs sempiternal in drones. . . . These fragments I shore to my shoal. . . . Inflicted and afflicted with community, the mirrored figment of one's self grown fictive in another's eye, the pigmentation of a man reduced to chiaroscuro, white telephone a chord uncut and constant ringing parody. . . . The parrot, covered, sleeps and can be silenced with a shade; we, bundled, merely toss to lie uncovered, tether torn. . . . Staggering from street light to hydrant and equivocally kind, we found in the titanic dust a separated early soul. . . . He called me son and slavered, "*Mon fils, m'en fiche, ta faim magnifique,*" and bowed to Astrid, belching, leaned against the window, fell. . . . Sir, he syed, ich biseche the, thatow woldest yive me that ich levedi briyt on ble that slepeth under the ympetre. . . . Recognition of causality comes late and last, is effect. . . . Lonely, insured, an excellent driver, the moon at its full and Cap Martin behind, geared to a nit-picking lint-faced guitarist, the radio waving "that ribbon of highway," Tom took the sea as a gift, unwrapped, and sea water seeps through thin slivers of silver, laps his tachometer now. . . . Maui was torn between the teeth of Hina-mui-te-po; the meat of immortality remains within her throat. . . . *"N'importe où hors de ce monde"*—any warehouse decent mind. . . . Meet my tables, set it down; I am a failure, failed. . . . This book alone I offer, altered at your altar, something the worse for where, terrible, bemused. . . . Gibber at the gibbet, cry: revenge, revenge, revenge—please greet your relatives. Solicitous, they burden you, hang (breach your breaches, sweep your chimney) me. . . . Identified by her dentist, Juanita Trapp, two years dead, lay skeletal, a three-inch knife beside her and her underclothing shreds. . . . "Bingo on Friday Nights, with the Exception of Good Friday." . . . The rooms are nine by twelve, transmuted into palace halls; clay ceilings seem as tapestry to the initiate. . . . Ingenious, ingenuous, what matter, you or I? . . . Veiled, reviled with words of promise, praise. . . . Myrtle and Arbutus were sweethearts; Algy wooed Plankton with weed. . . . Bonfires burn the winter scraps, that blighted countenance of Eden, tangled cherry trees. . . . (I must return to work. I must encounter Triapin and pen the man to paper like a moth. I must definitively show what prostitution means, demeans, the dancer and the dance, brief circuit flickerings that we, misguided, take for light. I must depict my second self and be the secret shearer of that dabbler double, him.) . . . The few small words that set us dancing—hope, trust, hate, lust, faith. . . . "Eighty-second Street," she said, "means screwing Harry Gideon." . . . Cane fires glow like villages within my mind's black sky. . . . The need to need was not specific, fastened to no single flesh; alternative beauties suffice. . . . Through the tall guns to the terrible grass. . . . Some women can accent their periods, call them a coma. . . . Mispunctuate punctual, late. . . . O-kuni-nushi and Susa-no-wo were masters of the Idzumo; Amaterasu, beneficent, from grief at her brother's ill-usage, stayed hid, a goddess sequestered from storm. . . . The plane trees by our patio give shadow to the house. . . . Carolus Quintus, attended by his sister, Queen of France, the Duke of Savoy, and others of his train, fell from a cracked plank to sea. . . . Then, happy low, lie down; blow wind from cheeks, from crack; the king lies uneasy at Villefranche, in silk. . . . In London, 1943, scrambling helter-skelter for shelter, I ate a piece of chocolate and still recall the wrapper, blown, seeming thrown. . . . Thus do we pad down our preordained paths, snow in a city, leaves on a lake. . . . *Et je m'en vais au vent mauvais. . . . Qui m'importe; n'importe. . . . N'importe qui? La fille morte.* . . . Is there no camouflage, comfort, protection, no recourse, *secours,* from the curse? Some women can assent. . . . We are born in blood and die bloodless; each seven years changed, plagued anew. . . . This seven-stringed lyre (my poor disjunct uncle, devoured by savages, scattered, digested) is lattice of roots. . . . Orpheo most of ony thing lovede the gle of harpying; syker was every gode harpoure of hym to have moche honour. He lernyd so, ther nothing was a better harper in no plas. . . . Egypt is a land of many mysteries. . . . Some squirrel must have come to share my firelit haven, winter's nest, 76 for each night I hear scrabbling and each morning find, accurately centered, in the hall, a nut. . . . Once upon a thyme spray lay my love, upon the sprig me prig, an aromatic her, an aromantic he: our very short story in deed. . . . Fidelity, I used to think, was harder far than faithlessness, and loyalty the greatest good of life. But I have written that book once already, and what remains without? . . . Eurydice. . . . To whom evacuate? . . . Dhanvantari held in his hands, cradled, the water of life. . . . From fear of inside seas, I make a drowning noise: clack-clack. . . . Adam's apple has stuck in man's throat; his gorge still rises at the fall; Eve's fruit, however, has multiplied; before, behind, in bloom, the seed. . . . I have a batch of titles here, to cover this work as a judge. . . . A Bird in Hand Is Worth Two in the Bed. . . . Beautiful Fire, Brocade. . . . Dutiful Fire Brigade. . . . Bocephalus Bridled (Again). . . . "The rustic, who seldom errs, pertinently remarks that it is too late to close the stable once the horse is out." . . . Shiva made the streams of Ganga wander through curls of his hair; Eochaid walked out upon the plain of Breg. . . . Manatee: A large, aquatic, herbivorous cetacean of the genus *Manatus*. Called also lamantin. . . . The crossroads at Antibes; I set a vein in my temple to beating, showed her my profile and obvious anger, let it beat ten times and cease. . . . This tongue in our sandwich of lips. . . . Presumptuous early mutterings such as Time is the Water of Lethe. . . . Brief as the prosy of a ring, your milk-and-honey promised hand. . . . The fait is in the fire. . . . Malory did time for political reasons and rape. . . . Savitri bought Satyavan from Yama, death, wrested poor resting husband bodily back. . . . Today I descended to Cannes, forgot the flaming festival and found myself engulfed—by flash-

77

bulbs and by dogs. The Croisette a small cross. . . .
A picture, *Hero Hercules*, dominated cars. . . . A man,
I read, was fined sixty francs for spanking his wife with
a live eel; one way or another, we pay. Soon spanning
elle shall be illegal, too. . . . Alexander in a diving bell
went down to plumb the depths; a diva belle, she-
serpent, crazed him naught. . . . Lord have mercy on
us. . . . Christ have merci onus. . . . Lord have mercy
onera. . . . The error of this era falls plurally upon us,
occasions penal code. . . . She noticed my thumbnail,
my ankles and eyes. . . . How blue they are with beg-
ging, red with pollen itch. . . . The sky itself stands
scutcheon to our house. . . . I, proud, shall feast on
scullions, fresh flesh, garnished leeks. . . . Three-headed,
seven-armed, Agni accepted oaths. . . . A fisherman,
wearing galoshes, net slung from left shoulder, goose-
steps down the beach; three boys pursue him, boxes
balanced on their heads, ten awed feet behind. . . .
Orpheus the fisher king could charm the woods to
follow, bend. . . . Bearded fig trees dominate the gully
of my mind, conquistador and rogue deluded, swing-
ing from a clove tree, purple-tongued. . . . Have you
encountered the regions of earth where ice never enters, tropical forests that never know snow, sand that
is always just sand? Such things, immutable, remain,
and trenchant we shall dig a ditch, fall in. . . . Phos-
phate; *fosse*-fate; food for the scavenger birds. . . .
Enterred in turn I shall stare at the sky, show spleen
to the vulture, a glacial deposit, a low-livered me; aloof,
alluvial. . . . While slow silt shifts, the specious species
go; while rain, encyclical, returns, I reste. . . . Do not
think I am dun; splayed simply on my back I shall
attend. . . . Each future festival and every trumpet call,
at the round earth's imagined coroners—a tintinnabu-

lation sounds but brass. . . . This equally, I promise you, shall pass. . . . Irène, the washerwoman, bloated nymph, mother to the problematic Aristide, rubs her finger on her upper gums and says. . . . Ich am an harpour of hethenisse; help me now in this destresse! . . . "My first husband, he was a man, with black hair and black eyes, a prominent man, but untrue, so I left him after eight months." . . . Not even M. Roget of flung Thesaurus' fame should weave words so assiduous, so tightly taut to tote; no pulp pap so deciduous, no forest for thee weary should extend. . . . This simply goes too far. . . . Ego-ridden, raddled, my book stands a riddle of rot. . . . One cannot dominate confusion but by clarity; upend a deadened log; observe the maggots crawl. . . . Scrawl contumely, contusion, on the proud stout limb; with time it too shall wither; the wise man plants acorns. . . . The rich man sows roses, the poor man potatoes; we sleep in well-earned sheets. . . . A worm winds in the urn. . . . Sing "Henry Martin" to a bairn, sing "Dink's Blues" to a babe. . . . Chant "Cotton-Eyed Joe" to a boll weevil, watch; he lookin' for a loam. . . . Larks nest in the print of a horse. . . . "The history of Cagnes is that of its chateau." . . . In my most need this night, I cry a lantern light. . . . Reduced to limerick, the search within me jars to jingle, consonance of consonants, a tale told by Diogenes, full of veins and fury, each artery unmined. . . . Bring water for the pan; shake sand; you find but a nugget of shale. . . . The fluttering bard of her throat. . . . Prospectus: this is phthisis, incantatory, cant. . . . Thor, dressed as Freya, ate eight salmons, killed the giant Thrym. . . . Geraint was the son of Erbin. . . . Excepting always and only the periods of peace when lulled by my own drone. . . . Long silence after speech. . . . Unable

even to bind. . . . Incompetent to bless. . . . A southern
soul-pole, lacquer, lack, a bee-loud glade in rain. . . .
Loki negotiates. . . . Always frantic, never busy, the
methodically inefficient. . . . Those cathedrals to bad
taste that stand erected, *whoribus*. . . . I do not know
whether compassion signals distance or proximity, comes
out of pity or fear. . . . Let them take the naked en-
terprise, a myth cloth, walking stick; me and my tatter-
demalion pals shall leave poetics, dance. . . . The second
Dionysus lies a slaughtered god; Athena holds his heart.
. . . Whip, viper, vibrant, woman all are cousins, as
flamingo is to oriflamme, and I to Zagreus. . . . He, that
hadde had castels and tours, river, forest, frith with
flours, now, thei it commenci to snewe and frese, this
king mote make his bed in mese. . . . (Note: occasional
music, chimes chime.) This world my oyster has occa-
sioned hepatitis, the virus still survives. . . . I know
it futile but need to see you, know it foolish but I want
to see. . . . Donne's siren song is elegie as you are
deade to me: oh, two convex contraries meet. . . . Out
of this juncture, disjunction, we must make, like grunt-
ling pigs, our meal. . . . (He was not what he seemed;
seem to have heard that somewhere, spoken of my dear
dead dad: scatter ashes will you kindly, on his head, the
sod. Repeatedly sacked, redoubtable, rare, does he bargain with worms, proposition the earth, split those cedar
sides? Lie lightly on him, clay; remember with rain you
are mud.) . . . Small mind, bent on the merely sugges-
tive, sickly drama mine. . . . Conceit cannot encompass
more than one slight circle, its organized *donnée*. . . .
How often has this fixed point lost centrality, each as-
pect of radiance dimmed. . . . I reverse Pygmalion; by
making statuesque, immobile, that which once was flesh,
I cure myself of need. . . . The sound of sea on stone.

... Circumscription, surely, is ascetic, not aesthetic; to defy, deny. ... In Digne, the Orphic deities are dead. ... The reasoned ritual of washing has grown difficult; how examine in each gobbet one's reflected self? ... Once, lightning there was anger; now, it is electrical, the meeting of two fronts. ... Nyx, great black-winged bird, bore Ouranos and Gaia in one egg. ... Bordering, protected solitude, the poet says, is love. ... Primarily pry merrily among the black-eyed, black-thighed ladies; live potted underneath the palms and bite the ripe breadfruit. ... Flamboyant trees will wave and waver, orchestrate the coral reef; still I dream of you deceiving, wonder where you, covert, covet, spread. ... All our righteousnesses are as filthy rags. ... Aëron and Conan slaughtered at Cattraeth. ... Congress of skin and sky emptied of pleasure, coition interrupted by the coming of the frost. ... No body, not even the rain. ... The dump is full of strange conjunctions, coat upon a stack. ... Our diplomatic thing plumes and pea-cocks, feathers its nest with a proto-call girl, is a divested interest. ... Lever me were to lete me liif, than thus to lese the quen mi wiif! ... One of those rooms which, aspecific, anticipates transience, its rotating owners like rosary beads. ... Serpents twine to Mithra, hover, cover, crave. ... Given one Christian, one Indian, and one name for each of her ratified husbands, she would be called Mary Coosaponakesee Musgrove Matthews Bosomworth. ... Urgency ordains these women bend beneath their thyrsi, bed beneath the wind that whets each dew-dulled slicing edge. ... Free Doom. ... Who is he that sits beside you, hand beneath your vest? ... Who is he that, after brandy, extricates your chest? ... Scraping and bowing, the waiter retreats. ... Sit with your back to the restaurant wall and think of Mary, dressed in musk, wearing only her Osnaburg shift, servicing the general, her nails split with stroking, hands caressed raw. . . . Enthusiasm is the penetrating god, his entrance in our mortal core, pearl after pearl mainlining, inserted in the blood. . . . That catechist was crucified with arrows in his grammar, blades across his pulse. . . . Ordering inordinate subordinates, *der Graf* contracted bitterly, was wafted to infinity, became a zero sum. . . . Where the piano tuner works, hammers sound in sheaths. . . . *Pelerin, pelerin, pelerin,* a three-hooved horse beneath me, and a pilgrim's age. . . . Passion scored those arms with reaching, scarred this mouth with song. . . . Thi bodi, that was so white ycore, with pine nailes is al totore! . . . "He wants to be intimidate with me." . . . Your lips, salivating ceaselessly, were firm once, flush-fleshed; now the lipstick covers only gum. . . . Suppose that Icarus continued, was not feathered with mere wax, but is the aspiration of each candle, guttering. . . . Imagine if those legs in Breughel were but adjuncts to a snorkel, and the sea would soon be emptied of its imitative equid, squid. . . . His separated head, as any artist's, 13,200 feet high, near Mount Erebus, Antarctica, above Ross Island, lava-laved, still singing, (inflamed, erysipelatoid, the pustules and the) soars. . . . A man is presumed to lose his innocence but once and then must act as if all-knowing; a woman must appear permanently innocent (innocent of permanence), surprised. . . . The dilettante escapes to work whereas the professional works to escape. . . . His conviction makes other people's taste, his taste their meal. . . . He hates the inexact, *das heisst, er hasste das ungefähr.* . . . The worst is when a sadness stops, when seeming eternity ends. . . . MacCecht found Conaire's son unharmed. . . . People lean when walking after

acts of love, articulate the selfhood shared, disarticu-
lation. . . . Kottos was the eldest of giants; Briareos,
Gyes hurled three hundred stones. . . . Shiran-kao,
which is the face of him who knows nothing. . . . We
are accustomed to meeting our previous partners, last
season's past affairs. . . . Likewise, the defiance with
which I finish my plate. . . . "Once, it was a big achieve-
ment to live here on the Concourse, a big step up in
life." . . . Law requires that seeing-eye dogs have access
everywhere but to the cinema. . . . Young men need
to be the first, and older men the last. . . . Xolotl knew
the evil willed by Mictlantecutli. . . . *Nada, amigo, nada.*
. . . If we embrace not beauty but failure, why am I
left alone? . . . Somnus came as Phorbas, beguiled the
steersman, pushed. . . . We shall grapple the tiller,
Attila, till hell turns into helm. . . . *Fléau de Dieu*
not five foot tall and wearing hair in braids. . . . Of
all the wonders that I yet have heard. . . . Halcyone has
perished with her Ceyx. . . . Each legitimacy banished
from my childhood faith. . . . We had four *fines à l'eau*
last year at Bramafan. . . . Finally, when these last
words are written, when we are complete, it still shall
be fortuitous, our separation, fall. . . . I cannot find
sufficient reason, cannot explicate; the text defies analysis, no arable parable this. . . . Deucalion and Pyrrha
cast behind them bones. . . . Cormorants cry, tinker
mackerel wriggle, and ringlets encompass that rock face
with sound; blanketing mist will not lift. . . . Is there
no balm in Gilead? Is there no physician there? . . .
Immutable and mute. . . . Pylades, Achates, we shall
not slumber, rinsed in sleep; the harvest is completed,
and we are not saved. . . . I know myself inconsequent,
stepped out of pace and place. . . . Loss, doom, decay,
and waste; what a sorrowful garland of words to have

garnered, gardened in my inland ardor, arid arbitrator, arboretor, fool. . . . The Münch and the Eiger, the Jungfrau, cloud-covered, a maiden I have not yet climbed, lie still. . . . A virgin forest, pal, is where the hand of man has not set foot. . . . Man seams and sows his suit of soot; this cord of cut wood is discord, a base abased, an ax to grind, a bower bowed, roof razed. . . . On August first, escaped, I drove to Switzerland. . . . Grenoble, Annecy, Geneva, Chateau d'Oex—I drove through Saanen, Schönried, Ringoldingen, Wimmis. . . . Ywain is the knight of no name. . . . I started at four in the morning, drove north, then wound all afternoon through the drenched valley roads, wet hills, where great cows cough, sheep low. . . . The sky was of lichen, of moss. . . . More serious than cirrus; mine, o thou lord of life. . . . I slept that festival sleep near the Trümmelbach Falls, down-covered, my balcony crisscrossed with flags, each dream dominated by flight. . . . Another green night of mine host. . . . Children with milk cans bicycled past; the village fires sputtered, smoked; Catherine wheels rainbowed to fall. . . . Red flame encompassed hilltops; men stood beneath their umbrellas to sing; the soft Swiss horns commended liberation, peace; it rained. . . . Go on, wan Gawain, accept her fox fur, box. . . . With dawn I left, returned. . . . The soaked wood waited in the lumberyards, pine piled, for trains that would not quickly come, and Spiez and Interlaken stood in fog. . . . Clotho has reduced each titan to her swaddling cloth; all things she measures, marks. . . . Except that I am driven by these syllable storms to howl, except that I am educated past recovery. . . . *Fata viam invenient*. . . . *Fatti maschii, parole femine*. . . . *Sans peur et sans reproche, sans beurre et sans brioche*. . . . Gwydion went with the swineherd to the

84

sow. . . . I am myself indifferent (therefore) honest.
. . . Mimir advised Oithin to journey to Vigrid. . . .
Hath the rain a father? . . . Vithar, the Silent God,
destroyed Fenrir the Wolf. . . . Metal is a good conductor but an awful engineer. . . . Riddled by complexity,
the simple story ends. . . . Shakespeare, shredded by
worms, relies on reprint rights so that his sonnet's boast
come true; this paper (glazed with the mildew to rot),
in a rainy season, cannot even flame. . . . Insatiate mechanics of meter with one serviceable song, the trouba-
dours of France prefigured each rhyme scheme. . . .
There are but three plots, someone said, and variations
on a theme. . . . I have had enough of all these public
people, personages, personae engaged in persiflage. . . .
Thimbleberry, goldenrod, the sweet wheat smell and
melon seeds. . . . Wives there lay on child bedde, sum
ded, and sum awedde. . . . Aristide attends to second
swarms and wax. . . . Royal jelly, he reports, beats honey
in Gourdon. . . . Incompetence, perennial, does not
desire solitude so much as gin slings and bountiful
ladies, a cat-nipped *canapé*, posed hose. . . . Man pro-
poses, woman supposes. . . . "Even moderation," we
simper, comfortable, "must observe its moderation." . . .
Put off the "chitoniskos" to convert and swim. . . .
Buoy bells clang in the swing of the sea, and a train
whistles, rounds the Corniche. . . . In Castellane the
sheep are sheared, and sky is as infected wool. . . .
Chestnuts come encased in spears, equality of mercy,
yet we eat a mound of maggot meat. . . . Presage of fall,
the figs grew; cover your shame and go forth. . . .
Crepitant, crepuscular, the valley of shadow extends to
thy sheep. . . . Swineherd, tend my flock of sleep and
govern declensions of dreaming; meretricious ladies
hike their hip-high frocks. . . . Wearing plaid knee socks.

. . . Substitute for Zeus a stone and watch his father feed. . . . Had I any instrument excepting this guitar. . . . They took Lucien and tortured him with oil, with wax, with knives. They slit his skin and tarred it, cut hands away, burned both wrists dry. They pulled at him with horses, but he would not break. They sawed through his shoulder and hips, separated him with ropes, hung the torso upside down in dust. . . . "He catched her by the yellow hair and drew her to the strand, but cauld an' stiff was every limb before he reached the land." . . . My child, my child, come screaming into sunlight, one hundred and eighty days old, blind, foot bent back and hand already wizened, bald, blighted from inception, from conception cursed. . . . The king is our father, the madhouse our house, for who would rather fardels bear, to swink and sweat in Heaven, Ga.? . . . As penitential offering, I humbled hang on you. . . . Clay cliffs crumble daily to sea; they bomb, buzz quarries now. . . . Sunflowers listless on their too-tall stalks drop, droop. . . . The forest fires flame. . . . A ship, a fish, a sailor, priest, cross, miracle, a name—I nail my work upon your wall and wait for sight of homeward sail: a widow's walk in wind, old king at Sounion. . . . Votive, the "plachzanitza" falls, devoted to Antibes. . . . Summer is upon us, blood, and celebrated August's mass surrounds the little church. . . . I hide in high burned hills, the memory of twin tipped mounds, and pray for your returning, rain, that each cloud scatter, burst. . . . *Le Phare envers enfer*, unfair, a charming sight, slight bight. . . . Hermit, hermetic within La Garoupe, prey, knave within the nave. . . . All is possibility, my work a pendant fruit. . . . Disjunction, dispossession, fear delimit the green apple of the bitter manchineel. . . . A knucklebone, a ball, tops, apples of the Hesperides, mirror, lumps of wool: with these they lured the god out of his childhood throne. . . . With four eyes looking this way and that. . . . With golden wings moving this way and that. . . . Tear a bull to pieces; eat near oak the new-raw flesh. . . . "Whenever thou shalt see him drunk with the works of the murmuring bees, then bind and fasten him." . . . All comes from One and is in One resolved. . . . To construct the world from the word one needs but an ell (that cockney perdition), a unit of length. . . . Sailors tattooed testaments upon their legs for fear of paper being drowned. . . . Better to have loved and lost than to have loved and won. . . . Aglaia, gracious one, grant mere civility. . . . No need to think that I am outcast from this earth; I get a letter from some friend or other each ten days; mechanics help me with the car, give oil; I saw the baroness again, still shave. . . . Astolpho was amazed. . . . One thousand years of Sibyl, wind among the leaves. . . . The people here have come to know me, not in full acceptance, but, passing, they raise hands. . . . Hast thou thy Maker forgot? . . . Why so pale and won? . . . I watched a woman drink eau de cologne, call it water, sleep. . . . Open Pandora's box and find a Trojan horse. . . . My ship, this wave stallion, paws toward shore, is coming (you once chorused) in. . . . Whither art thou going thus gaily? . . . Everyman assumes the garment of contrition. . . . Caswallawn slew six men. . . . Histion, the son of Japhet, had four eponymous sons. . . . Manal; of or pertaining to the hand, adj. . . . The single instrument of our out-going and in-coming, of out-coming and in-going. . . . Muse, let's sing of rats. . . . And maidens with swelling breasts the same age as themselves. . . . Hippomenes and Atalanta are yoked to Cybele. . . . Majesty in ermine goes beating cup and crutch before the awful onslaught of white age. . . . Maral is a Persian red deer. . . . There is no photograph can render this variety, spindrift. . . . Of the manatee, it further must be said: the stomach is complex. . . . He hadde with him a quen of priis, that was ycleped dame Heurodis; the fairest levedi for the nones that miyt gon on bodi and bones. Ful of love and of godenisse, ac no man may tell her fairnisse. . . . Debt-ridden, plagued with the impractical, survived by no new generation, sonless, violin-playing ghost of a wind-strung night, architect of the Big House and his own ruin, dueling, Gwinnett possessed, at death, a saddle horse called Chickasaw, mahogany beds, a wife, one of three engendered daughters, books by Blackstone, Junius' letters, cartridge paper, a dress sword, spyglass, two volumes on agriculture, decanters, a yawl, and sixty-one slaves. The wife was named Ann, the daughter, Elizabeth, the slaves, among others, Caesar, Cato, Wednesday, Lazarus, Mingo, Franklin, Cupid, Phyllis, Fanny, Quanimo, Sam—the yawl, *Beggar's Benison*. . . . Fatuous memories throng, enthrone deception, the self-serving altered self (*introibo ad altare mei*) stately pump where once was a slipper silvered in ash. . . . The unpurged images, like Triapin's hairline, day, recede. . . . As best you can: initiate novitiates alone. . . . Who if I cried would listen to me then from out of the orders of angles? When water hits the poop, follow rats. . . . And that the Shinto deities might favor your petition, wash garments in a stream. . . . Lay a pallet on the floor (preceptively simple); palatable pullets should be stewed. . . . Digest but the fertilized egg; sleep twenty-three hours a day. . . . Empty your bladder in pots. . . . Stretch a sword by your side if she snores. . . . Attain the superconscious through the conscious; scratch where it itches, and bawl. . . . All quiddity is gone from me, all flippancy, frippery done. . . . No mythic figures frolic down my saddened manic mind. . . . Except to sing and stop, he hath not mouthed a syllable; leaves grate, berate the door. . . . Consider moats made out of sand; not even that I achieve. . . . These filaments that file like wire in my work, the light-motifs, loss, suicide, these strains I, tortive, stress, strands weave. . . . A book about chaos and (*avant tout fût*) night. . . . We all have our private diseases, are proud of disorder within, and mine defies diagnosis, the number on point of a pin. . . . Too suffering, injured, inured: an Atlas with *Angst* upon shoulders and dead. . . . I am too pill-lightheaded to be polite; a sissy fuss over gallstones . . . . Nebuchadnezzar was the king of Babylon (should rack me, shock a bent ego). . . . Place all the Hebrews in the fiery furnace (sad rock, me shackle, bed nigh go). . . . Lambs graze at Coursegoules. . . . Feted, fetid, fat id. . . . This is a parlous parlor game involving merely me. . . . Solly Loquee down the street instructed how to play. . . . Super-charade: I talk and talk, you guess what act I mean, which mien. . . . Ygdrasill, the mighty ash. . . . Asgard is the home of the gods. . . . Where oxen pace apace i'space. . . . Why must we maul each other so, moose buffeting, mantises, devout, devoured whole? . . . In this climate, climacteric, climb upon your hobbyhorse and ride. . . . We are a whoreson, churlish lot, the gift of light a theft. . . . That poor, kind, henpecked fool. . . . If I had had more than this wisp of a will, whippoorwill. . . . Deiphobus was illusion, not at Hector's hand. . . . Maulardes, hayroun and comeraunt, the foules of the water ariseth. . . . Flagship of the fleet. . . . When, as a shattered gong, thou noisest not.

. . . When me and a bunch of cowboys. . . . Gode is the lay, swete is the note. . . . On All Soul's Day, in 1873, burned fell the branch and seasoned hell of poetry was ash. . . . The seven steps to transmutation, wheel within a wheel, circumference of cliffs. . . . Water comes from earth and souls from water come. . . . Oh, Captain, mercaptan, thy feral fear is stench. . . . Proteus pastured sea calves. . . . One poem (maybe as cold and compassionate, the nightly ramble through the purple patch, Freud's fields) dawns within my ice cube now, looks very like an olive, its pit gone soft and red. . . . Orfeo was a king, in his time an heize lording, a stalworth man and hardi bo, large, curteys he was also. . . . Sayadio recaptured, lost his sister in a cup. . . . Caricature of godhead, joy, impuissant, unperturbed. . . . *Strahlend und fatal.* . . . The single error, parting, we may not recall. . . . Committed to commiserate, *komm mit.* . . . Our two selves separate; give the cat a tonic, let her mew. . . . A woman interviewing candidates for the position of chauffeur, etc., asks but one question, to chafe her, two chauffe: "Let's see your qualification." . . . The lovely old women in furs, the lovely young men in the lovely old women; my friend is the King of Morocco, my brother the queen of Oran. . . . I say let that aye sty smolder, rot; how am I reduced to cackle, a gaggle of goslings; sit, ducks. . . . Is it possible these notes are but jokes, a long obscene pun upon farce, dotted with eyes, crossed tease? . . . What sad taskmaster sets me duncing, musters debate up in sky? . . . What did God do with himself before Eve, and how, when she left his good garden, clothed, weeping, did he solo, consortless, console? . . . Digital diarrhea, this type. . . . Cease. . . . Cease. . . . See. . . . No man should wear wool to a temple nor calf leather

bound to his feet. . . . This obsessive intrusion of self.
. . . Bot his harp he tok algate, and dede him barfoot
out atte yate. No man most with him go. . . . Murder
in a ping-pong match and terror on the tennis court;
diverse divers versify. . . . Irrigators guide the water;
fletchers mold the arrow and man makes himself. . . .
Marry, an honette coquette cast her net for a marion-
ette. . . . The single untorn gown is that which is un-
worn. . . . Cleanliness, gossamer veil. . . . Sensible,
discretionary, meditative, grim. . . . This, the eleventh
month . . . . Council; count, sell. . . . Latent, not
blatant . . . . Even true memory falters. . . . Vague
vagaries collect. . . . The southern face of Shiva is the
face of death. . . . Five useful fingers and four walls,
the circumscription of a cell, Cervantes, even so. . . .
We need such reassurance, mirrors by the bed. . . .
Izanagi observed his woman in the Place of Gloom:
her forehead was a bone. Izanami was angered, and
the Primal Pair disjunct. . . . Farther I shall arise in
my auto daffy, crash my bodily decrepitude to ash,
whiz dumb and deaf to all entreaty; give credence to
the passed. . . . A part of you is with me still, apart we
maintain partnership, a common program-pogrom and
par terre . . . . The Judas goat enters the pen. . . . He,
that had kniytes of priis before him kneland and
levedis, now seth he nothing that him liketh, bot wilde
wormes bi him striketh. . . . Mrs. Cheynesworth-Hudson
sent somehow here an invitation to her daughter's
Dallas coming out; why would'st she be but a breeder
of sinners; keep her, Mrs. Cheynesworth-Hudson, well
(in clothes) enclosed, encased (in case). . . . Lickspittle
lover of parentheses am I; consider mole tunnels
crudescent in sand. . . . Lugalkidia is both a fish and
the red writing table of Bel. . . . I do not wish to

strew-spew (partridge, startled, flee) nor closer to construe . . . . "You have no character" is the reproach the mediocre level at the excellent. . . . Inception of deception marks the end of trust . . . . How conscious was Deianeira when she poured the blood of Nessus, vengeful or deceived? . . . Regret, fervid and febrile, consummate, consumes. . . . In abnegation and abasement, in a cellar even, humbled, we clown. . . . Strange secrecy of revelation, pointing the first finger (all heel and no Achilles), dirty truths cleansed, claimed. . . . I cannot think that once I ate the meat of cattle, fowl flesh, wore their skins on mine. . . . Ixion might roll within the wheel of birth for some such sin or less. . . . When the thousand years will once more circle, close. . . . And the honorable works of nature, eternal and boundless, stand fast. . . . Wife and children are as hostages to fortune. . . . What, that petty coat depleated, all thy pretty ruffles roughed? . . . Eels dominate my mind. . . . There are those placed on this world as hosts, and those who come as guests. . . . Man is idolized, woman idealized; they, the pragmatic sex. . . . And when he his harping lete wold, no beest bi him abide nold. . . . Long-lived as the feathered palm . . . . Many the wand bearers, few the Bakchoi . . . . The absurd last remnants of association, song snatches (go away from my window, away from my door), smell, elbows stained with drink taken together. . . . God is not a man, that He should lie. . . . Tell it not in Gath, publish it not in the streets of Askelon . . . . Doggerel is but a rhyme in time. . . . I am but the prelude; after me, they delude. . . . The ruddiness is all. . . . *Fiat experimentum in corpore vili.* . . . In my short life, I have not seen an *ars longa* than hers. . . . Puns punctuate connections that we could not else make, break. . . . Must every archer fester, stink, wet wounds to draw a bow? . . . Ribbons might suffice; Aristaeus taught the management of bees. . . . In the cool tomb grant rest, now and in the hour of our *ave atque vale*. . . . Nebuchadnezzar thought himself an ass, ate grass, which never is greener than grace. . . . Town names are altered, even; undying sorrow, inaccurate label, a libel, must make way for Midway, is dead. . . . If you are misspelled, forgotten, or misplaced, forgive; a raindrop has blurred you past sure recognition, like time.

3

ZAGREUS
RECONVENED

Through forgery Hephaestus pottered, stumbled, puttered, passed. Perpetuating the betrayal of his house and spouse, he fashioned (it behooved him) a set net. The saddest moment of the myth comes in that confrontation: Aphrodite naked and the cuckold cursing Ares—an artisan imprisoning despair.

Do you hear me summon you; Heraclitus knew division, exploration with no explanation, particles made manifest, particular and whole. The hippopotamus is sequel to the square. Of the sum of the parts, Astrid said, keep your books in rows.

Art is cohesion, coherence, concomitant with opposites, and I am at that northern pole. Where chaos, dark last six straight months, seal blubber lights the ice. *Qui est'ce qui* moans so lonesome, low; when will we decompose? Untracked, intractable, an Orpheus six months ineffective, merged with Morpheus, I squat upon this floe-flow, float. In the beginning was Ginnunga-gap; Baldr the Well-beloved lived in Breithablik. The Aesir settled in Asgarth and made peace with the Wanes. My only companions are dead, each glad associate unreal, and every mythic friend I name has never uttered mine. How can we be so private, so fetuslike abed, so curled around our feces, anal, analogical, such ships that press at night? We imitate, intimate intimacy; you do not know my name.

A beak-nosed whale washed to the village shore and died; children spin themselves a skein, a circle, fall. Penelope, perfectionist, pulled wool upon her distaff side, undid each suit with trumpery, most seaming-virtuous queen. Put off thy willow weed and weep: the cocks at dawn, tumescent, spawn.

Improvisational, we shift from pillar to past, from frying pun to fire, from the truth to Ruth. If all were once more clarified, and the night not ugly, I could keep, from dark dominion, free. Forfare, voyager, thy hecatomb forfeit; the gods, athirst, drink nectar of a neck.

In any but this escalating century, just to be was to suffice, to endure was to illumine, and a Book of Hours three years' work. One needed not to rise, surmount; Abelard the anxious became an apse of lard. Castiglione detailed courtesy, and many a courtier earned castle, his keep. The rain it raineth every day; Cordelia and the fool were one, play-favorites alike. A liking, bootlicking, a dropped cloak in puddle could give the world the lie, could well suit a suitor while yet his face pleased. They knew no equal urgency, ancestral shades beneath the oak yoke, harmonizing spheres. There was a place for cuckoos in the universal clockwork, gold enameling, and such a form as Grecian Smithies make. I could wish it still so: now Raleigh pushes weeds.

How may I suggest that marriage stands as symbol (treat a woman as you would a new-dead dog; immediate replacement works the remedy for grief), that entrusted to her was my every young ideal—her ankles were emblems, her wrist a result—that with this long dismantling I attempt to grow? There was a little girlie and her name was Veer-aye-go.

Stranger, do not tarry, rest at Villeneuve-Loubet. Viracocha, as a beggar, was known by his child. He cursed the parrot, blessed the falcon, grieved beside the sea. Every creature living breathes in fealty. The long hegemony of darkness weights, awaits you, traveler: mourn.

Land crabs scuttle back to hide and lizards scatter where we walk; in desire's alchemy, here is there and now is then. Brain coral offers an accurate image: stone submerged in memoriam, sea.

Patrician ladies, equally, smoked cubebs out behind the barn; *te petens Palinure.* Thou art Peter; thou and a baker's dozen rocked my rolled religious wife, were spires when she sparred. By the waters of Vichy I sat down and whipped. By the daughters of Clichy I sat down and sipped. Nowhere do we find sufficient convocation, nor does form convene.

Our new dimension, energy; space strewn like blankets about a used bed, sheet spread upon the floor—art is limitation; drawing, lines. How stand we so delimited, a series of sentences

99

passed. Restrictive cause-clause collating colons, quota of quotes, quotidian word graft—with meter as parameter, our language seems paragraphed phrase. I could wish to write the moon as if it were moon moon. Speech is split infinity, sustained mixed metaphor: moon, lunaticlike, means cheese, a dead star, man in the, June, Diana, satellite. A nimbus, rhombus wreathed in limbo, galaxy of parallel sound; we should have had our tongues cut out, used hands. The palette of our palate winds, and correspondence, a serpentine turpentine, cleaves ("My nose feels red," she said). Words were invented to silence song, are noise.

Old men forget, misplace. Young men embroider ikons that they cannot long remember, uniform as cuneiform, a laundry bill in clay. I have seen the wind blow smoke into the mouth of fire, file those teeth into submission, shame my tongue with space. Your image will recede with each October, fade.

Today again most sober, somber, I tally my tale, three beads on an abacus, stranded success. These are wounds that were his eyes; broach the brooch upon cat feet, impoverished, and press. Laius and Jocasta had one ungrateful son. A peripatetic peripeteia, clogged cognition cog; he shall clutch at his crutch as a staff. An agon, Anti-agony, anagnorisis; the fool and his gold are soon sundered; earth has not anything to show but azure, ice, and birds. Extinguish flame, Etienne, we are too poorly armed.

That I must so disguise what is emotion merely, so riddle my confession with the artifice of art, is emblem both of cowardice and form, dear reader, form. Mind accrues to matter as the wart hog to the wart. My wish was but to mutter that I am a town invaded; shame has set me ciphering and loss is labyrinth now. At the center of maize remains corn.

A book of dreams, *Tibetan Dead,* coincide upon my pillow, where this morning (and some squirrels woke me, scrabbling at the roof) I imagined bacon leavings, bicycle spokes, Triapin dressed as Arab and an open page of Proust. What could be less powerful than other people's dreams or, by extension, other people's waking fiction; I no longer summon the patience to read, cannot require readers of my own so-tedious text. That I hallucinate my mother in each upraised glass, my father in each garbage lid, that leafless trees recall Thanksgiving when I dropped the yams in soup would interest an analyst at best. God, in Genesis II, that primitive potter who stalks into Eden, merits worship and libation; he who, in Genesis I, fashioned the world out of word was idolatrous and merits merely grief. Penitence can be a public thing, group therapy with whips and scourges for the company—"The value of solitude," Triapin said, "is only as contrast, that people should see you alone." The elaborate game that we flagellants play, comparing scars, constructing shame, tracing welts with crayon onto a bent back, palls, bores. Display is deep temptation and fools follow rules; I curl myself to this cocoon and, fatuous, feast on absorption, consider the present a span between shores.

Orpheus dissenting voyaged eerie waterways, evinced through nasal passages the four recurrent syllables of his wife's single name. From uvula to larynx, water lapped at his held lip; crabs pulled at his nostrils and picked at his eyes; still he sang Eurydice and the Hebrus flowed, cortege and corpse interfused.

(I am more an antique Ottoman than Danish pastry, furniture. I am more an antic Otto than a Smorgas broad. The drowning sun in a green sea—nothing is bitter, something is rattan—was this the face that frights off angels, lunched on thousand shrimps?)

Upon a slope, ten miles beneath the Pré-Alpes, ten miles from the sea, with olive trees above, below, and cyprus, scrub pine, oak, fresh water piped from foothills and white roses on the wall, with stone upon the old tile roof, anemones outside, our home was sweet, hearth, rock. Two churches we had, but with discordant clocks; one ever would offer three minutes of grace. My table made of oak, with water rings on wood, remains, and here, by the mimosa, lies my head. (Wasps put up no struggle as the spiders kill. It is partly from fear of your full comprehension that I so spread the seasons, dislocate recovery and time; a rune of ruin to present, disperse this riddled year.)

History repeats itself for the simple and sufficient reason of historians; how explain a cause but by its sole effect? There is nothing new under the novelist's sun, no word waste uncharted, unchartered, not one song unsung nor story untold. Yet for the single instance of Astrid's departure, I could instanter instance twenty explanations, twenty fragments round a silent splintered center, each inadequate. Where in the evidenced welter hides fact, which of these shadows joins substance—all, none? I feel most apoetical this evening, shall leave the answer to rhetoric, bunk, history, shall dream. "It's certain that fine women eat a crazy salad with their meat," certes, licorice. Take this thy physic, metaphysician; true apothecary, know we are subtracted and abstract. Jewel facets of fiction cannot fascinate those who lie; I am the night-mayor of all I survey and (by its formless spawning gong-tormented filthy modern tide) survive.

Distance looms unbridgeable; even in each other's arms, we but approximate proximity, uncover chasms, span. So permanent a parody of union was our bed, that battlefield of selflessness and spite, that I, recalling, writhe to write—communion of a mass with mass is coarse investiture, asseveration, intercourse.

A woman is attracted by the problem posed, the chase; she lives resolved to solve. What is more perverse than that the Sphinx should have been tamed by comprehension, angered at those men who could not understand? She was but half a female or would have done the opposite, devoured Oedipus. Mystery stands instinct with the sex; Salome took off seven veils before she showed her heart.

Duplicity our might main-word, all oaths stand oafish, offish, conned; nor conjurer, magician, fake can disavow, how sheer prestige of prestidigitation sways us still. To contravene is venal, renal; Merlin laughed three times. We always cheat at cards, hunt for the rabbit in hat, hatch hutches in silk purse; we disconnect linked rings and watch. Abacadarian, abjured, we learn by what is rote.

103

I used to think that writing was creation, that the hand, analogous to Buonarroti's god, reached out to infuse energy, was green force forced, pristine, Sistine, was liberator, parent, aid —that characters could grow and move, dimension shift, surprise. Not so; the artist must embalm. He must fix on fed flame; the rest is smoke, is ash. Fled fame alone attends those who attempt this life; a fact seen through prison-prism goes fictive, and six equal shadows obtain. Heraclitean, surmounting sermons spring from fire, bodiless, impermanent, a forked tongue emblazoned on air: sear, seer. The passenger moment transformed, the transient found and bound in heat is my fit study, school, the decor of decay. I know no alternative now; we must scrape for scraps, tell truth.

A clenched fist shaken in the cosmic face is man, an irritant and errant ant, presumptive of the very air and heir to sand hills merely ("We give Green Stamps," titled an episcopal bulletin), dry salvaged ego immersed in its muck. Three savage men forgot first-person pronouns once, and that was a singular day.

Immoderate, ranged beyond all modulation, ringed as though some captive teal might cross the Northern Sea (thy hands are a harvest of honey, thy forearm a portion of wine), we fester in each fetter, disavow each bond. I must revert to villages, scale myself anew, know boundary, earth oath.

The Emperor, returning, did not stop at Grasse; the mayor of that city sent no welcome key. Prudential, nonetheless, he offered Bonaparte refreshment at his country house—(You never can tell, said the wife). Observe those callous burghers still; they wave white handkerchiefs; the ragamuffins tread on what might soon be bread.

You, my necessary angel, were, *wenn ich schreibe,* transitively there. Pass through the circle into flame and purge; an onion has no (hear it in the deep heart's) core.

I imaged Eldorado on the hills this morning; framed by the geodetic tower and a stationary hawk, twin-spired, it rose, an address on Central Park West. Illusory paradise of parapets and mirrored halls where elevator men wear braids and carry their bottles in bags, where poodles soil the carpeting and wigs hang from mop handles, city of golden linoleum streets, heaven-aspiring hearths—it hovered by the olive trees, then toppled to the roots. A bridge made out of toothpicks and straw won an engineer's prize; what of the constructivist that makes a book out of miasma, morel nursed out of decay?

Children weaving carpets in Iraq do not count stitches but know, eidetic, patterns in advance. The sense of time intrudes again when patterning comes clear (this is the fabric of my life, a speech of angered age); I recognize eight parallels, embark upon the ninth. What force of fatality has so designed me that I should tremble, treble back; why should this rapt and inward-wrapped warp-woof in weave recur? This morning's hundred words evade me by twenty per cent; predictable, I am but a figure enwrought.

105

From sheer servility of manner we continue to praise matter, act as if some content may be found in strong contention, try to prove kinetic that which always stays the same. My father died, and his father before him; earlier, by some few years, they wailed into this world. What subject, philosopher, can you find there beyond the subjectivity of change?

Plague is a comparative, and only Sam escaped. The wide wale is a corduroy and not leviathan. The President ordained his kidney stay unphotographed, and magazines were shocked. Cleanliness and goodliness are leased upon the land; palimpsest gone pallid, show character, hold hand.

I think continually of those who truly grate, that damned elusive pimp, kernel of nutmeg flaked in rum, come see Jerusalem (wires cut the Via Dolorosa, the church there is pillbox, the campanile armed); tradition is a root that reaches into sand. "It's boring to be old," the old man said. "I'm bored here, everywhere." White skull bent to the breeze, he hobbled back to shore. Battened palm fronds cover him; chiropodists arrive.

Beyond this auto-amputation, the technique of surgery, there lies some small clinical residue, some incision in indecision, aim. I know her inadequate, easy, and cheap, a woman wasted, spoiled; my end is to finish, exorcise all spirits, bloodlet. I shall wear blue beads only; thumb between fingers, I shall make a poultice, brew bruise. Why stay so shackled to disease, examining vitals, intent; why marry marred miss-calculation, sluttishness, mistake? Incite insight; the mold has gone moldy and form infirm; smooth marble has mottled (not gamesome and gallant), has stippled to clay. Each final piaster of poverty spent, she shall beggar description, bang cup.

My father moved through rooms of love and would not longer be a Montague. Linger in the passages, empurpled by prose, of infancy's (cast a cold coal on bulbous Ben) labyrinth. Once the wall was shadowed flame and feet lay lanced by hedgehog quills. Once sea urchins clung to red Le Trayas rocks; cantankerous horseman, pass by.

Consider if the coupled beasts, paired, spared within the ark were sterile—nothing could prevail. Perhaps some antiquated female covered by the covenant and covetous of offspring could not bear; he doomed (her panting partner) to clamber, delve in vain. Conceive the fecund deluge then, and how those forty nights would mock gestation, multiply. Nourished by nurturing rain, the olive tree gives forth; doves dive; Noah, unfortunate husband, has nonetheless fathered this world.

Wiglaf, king enough to kill, could yet not rescue, save; Bedlam shames the name of Bethlehem; wasps sting themselves insensible; trees split. How many citizenries must each man renounce; what allegiance is there to maintain? Sleep, thou sovereign leveler, we kneel to thy least Nell.

The monotonal moon tone, Thomas, is Qlipoth, and Antony when dying hauled by ropes to hell, chattering through scree

and down to Erceldoune, while Eridanus, rising, swallows po'
Phaeton, and evil involutions of evolution's vulgar vulva, flow
—"I have a double uvula," she said, and opened wide.
"Observe, where once my wisdom teeth tore, struts."

Upon a polka-dotted wall there hangs a mandolin. Is it a trick
of eyesight or revealed reality that inches to the left I find,
outlined in polka dots, the instrument again? Bodiless, it hovers
on the paper, holds; the shadow image of itself, a prescient
presence near. One definition of imbalance might be merely
this: those who, as myself, discover substitutes for substance,
hear the echo, not the word, maintain nor poise nor equipoise,
note in each departed mind the matter of decay. I would not
live with those who figure forth the mandolin on every papered
wall, nor do I choose to mark the actual alone. Between the
physic and the psychic there stands but a sea. See, Plato, how
we have concluded thy division; normality dictates—the abnor-
mal abdicate. There never was a leg belonging to the sandal
she forgot to pack. The three taut wires shiver, twine, intestines
of a cat.

How happy we could be to proffer a continuum, to tell a
plotted moral tale, give dialogue and dialect, to serve three
unities. The continuity of Satan is our most poetic loss; we
have no dearth of satin nor dervish-devilish imaginings; the
prosody of this perpetuated sentence leaves nothing so desired
as a stop.

Say farewell to Paros, and figs, and seafaring life; this tomb-
stone lies if it says that it points to the place of my burial.

(Mistral, given half a chance, could blow that massif to the sea. I, Ahasuerus, could use a cup of tea.)

Facinorous, hederated, cheap; a fish-net suit she wore, with no underclothing, and, "During the Rape of Lucretia, while for three minutes he lay atop me, and eight hundred watched, I could hardly breathe, he weighed so much and stank"; *no se puede beber sin beer-beer.*

Copt Amarilla, aye, the white breast dimly see: all withers wither (what male stalked through the post office then?), shanks shrink. Lepanto left our master maimed; for God's sake let us sit.

Prehensile, we hold to the life line and onto the cliff face adhere. Endurance our primary passion, the oldest amongst us revered (though treated with that scorn which somehow survivors deserve, as if they did not fight, or waged an easy war, or were too battered in the process to instruct), and out of each Thermopylae we draw a mural-moral, pin it to the wall. Home Is Where the Hearse Is. God Rust Ye, One and All. What private assurance have we received against senility that we should haste so headlong into that slow slope? Rome was not built, did not wilt in a day; gibbous, I sing of the gibbet, decline. Perhaps in seven years, altogether altered, no particle of my new body recollecting you, I shall be competent, trailing clouts of gory-story, to allocate locusts, begin.

Again I came to Cannes, surrounded by society, a conversation piece. The mark upon Cain's forehead did not so much show him an outcast as assert his previous disgust, the blood so boiling in his brow that excess had to spill. Take a pariah testimonial: peace is a hopeless conservation, even if Zeus, the god of rain and company, minded pees and queues. Take any two men, doctor, put them in a room, add one woman, stir; you have two enemies. Diplomacy is wrong; the way to save this world is through engirdling walls, gulfs, Guelphs, that man may not look out and spy his brother, kill. It is not distance but proximity that occasions horror; I ran down the Rue d'Antibes.

Need can be so imperative it grows directionless, an urgency so all-embracing it exceeds containment, cannot be relieved. We are anonymous as dust. For these occasional angers, I ask your pardon, humbly; for the loss of kindness, I am most ashamed. Monkeys clamber down the siding, enter through the shivered window, watch the slivered skin of passengers fall, flap. Skittering from handle to platform, excited with ruin, they stare.

That the bard should be blind stands as critique and as correlation; whether Homer was a woman, six men, single harper, harpy, prince, whether Milton used daughters as candlesticks, Joyce dreamed in off-color, Oedipus wrecks—seers they were all, discerning word shape, sound. The auditory image, grave not graven, site un-scene, citation of cities to conjure them there (how primitive, still, our belief in the word, that once spoken it works, effectual, once uttered it acts, enacts—"I do not need you any more," screamed beyond retraction; "get out of my life, my wife")—these things are common to the eyeless, constant in their chant-cant (raze your glasses), song.

110

Fructify or frutify, all good men are borne to die; evil is the emptiness that strives to empty others; open your window to warm up the winter, embrace plasmolysis. Through this membrane, memory, we pass as water, shrink.

Have you heard the deaf and dumb speak, thought, through doors, that love was murder, seen a seeming corpse that was newspaper blown? Bring no more vain oblations as the turtle, voiceless, turns to soup; wine, labyrinthine, leads to stupor, a mock supper, body bread. Symbolic, symbiotic, a nexus of meaning, barnaclelike, attaches to the devil spar and spurns the deep green sea, joins nerveless ganglia. Fingers twist and curl to tell a letter and a line; in the beginning was void.

In the whale trough, cry: (nothing, her mouth) out of irritation, sand, we pry such cultured pearls. Sell each secretion to hang round a neck; the albatross poet weighs anchor encore, wings.

Caparisoned, the whores trot past and offer for comparison their forelock, fetlock, teeth. Upon a pebbled beach, beneath a split-shale ledge, observe the bones of deer, cows, dogs, the carcass of a sheep. Know that we are shriven, driven; see the cancer rattle, color tongues.

From pillow to bedpost, truant, pursuant, from Theon's frying Pan, with no moderation, we flee, sprawl free, sink once again

111

anointed, appointed: aroint. Thou, Satan, art the very devil of an agitator, filthy fiend; drop a quarter in the slot and this whole bed vibrates. The coverlets co-ordinate with curtains and are brown.

Given the existence of pebbles and a personal lord (with white beard with sight bleared a bar bit you rate), what put thee over all sin misses Murphy's chowder; what putty, that pity, unfinished lament. Were I to truly tell all ill about my heart, thou wouldst not think, Horatio, thyself content to bridge— the gap between providence, fall is too great; a special sparrow harkens to the hawk. Kali desires a knot in your throat, or, preferably, on. By Jove, he is, thy god, a jealous, vengeful cove. As Zeus of the strangers he came and departed, was with us a wile and has gone. When no man knows this oar, I shall be sufficiently distant from sea, can play with my paddle, lie down.

Forewarned is disarmed, a triolet error; men, legless, hop away from trucks where once trains sliced, hack-sawed. This is not a novel but an epi-tome; news, age. As the cat i' the adage turns tail, dogs hobble homeward with a tin can tied, and my third line is seventh life and first.

In Mougins where the mighty shop one cannot ask for alms. Sign this paper, blacksmith, testify to grace. Jamshid the Resplendent may prosper once again. Regarding this slight leak, it scarcely ever rains; larks nest within the ruined tile while greasy Joan doth keel and kneel: cultivate your guard.

112

In Vallauris the clay-cake burns and Bessie lows affrighted with the smell. Around the Madoura we imprecate the implicated air. Heigh-ho, in a bite of thy ample apple I would wallow-swallow, delight. Let us engender, fortify, the wedding of flesh, blood; December is when all good soldiers die.

In Cabris where the wolves once ran ears furled against the wind (and when their ribs were scaffolding upon the incompleted structure of a meal), I, argal naught, wandered with you as companion (have some golden fleece, m'deah), and now the rich snore sweetly, take (a dram perchance to dream).

In Cap Martin, Dionysus lies down to sleep at four; around him in their undulating chorus line Choephoroi libate. An oblate bait they offer to this century of centaurs; cheesecake in a mousetrap, entrails, spoil. When Nietzsche comes to look at this lewd contrast to Apollo, he will be appalled.

In Ste. Maxime, Lachesis strummed strung inundation, thrummed her banjo belly to the beat of larval lava, ash and flood. Fatted policemen neared the Fate and, noting her shear stockings, were bemused. They tried to arrest her and dally, could not, for, drumming up her business, she drove to St. Tropez.

In Hyères, Wallace and Sal sang fa-la to the moonlike lamp, initiating galaxies of current and night light. The old proprietor observed them and forebore to smile; they continued, nonetheless, to howl fa-la, fa-la.

With a bow to Sterne and poop, with a look at Locke and home, let me describe the wad man widowed when he made from wattles, clay:

Triapin insists that art act as a servant, come at his first beckoning, earn reckoning, urn keep. If it be his hard mistress, I have yet to note the cruelty; if it be his Circe, I have yet to see the charm. Consummate showman and swine, the man bids me credit his trough full of truffles, applaud.

Do you see, in this triangle, how congruent we are of shape, how similar, eternal is the base, rise, intersection—how thoroughly Euclidian our posture, postulate? To be, above all, to thy sweet self true; an accidental axiom, fostered by our Faust, host of the hoist petard: those that are married already, all but one, shall live. An ox, disoriented, plodding the same circle, scatters a bucket of salt-sweet sweat for each water bucket upraised; husband the earth, shed seed. When Kronos castrated his father, the Romans mispelled time. They thought him Chronos, whence chronic, whence sickle (wince, chthonic), which just goes to show: you need a blade to bring blades low, and at the point of contact, genitals on she-sea, see: Aphrodite born. Not as is this book palace, Pallas, full-blown from out of my fathering brain, already armored, girt—but gentle, clothed in zephyrs, foam, pink wrists upturned to praise. Sing sweetly, choiring cherubim, inquire will she sell the shell? Wouldst throw herself into the bargain, barge into my largess, barge?

Caprice, so seeming brilliant, glisters to no purpose in an emptied hall; the different drummer, forced, conscripted, hears no social beat and heeds no antic, attic grace when sky fills fat with wind. Dance to your light measure, pages on parade; I tried to light a fire with four legs for sticks.

Hephaestus should be god of art, not merely artisan; he has been tempered in the crucible, dipped, stripped. Profane, we feign emotion and, polite, pollute. I am lying, Egypt, lying, with the poverty of Hope; she asks, and two thousand leer for the labor, no recompense but joy.

The voice that cries and echoes in the wilderness should be disembodied, own nor name nor throat. We do not listen to the talker; we regard his soapbox, stare. My occupation's gone, my birthplace is not now my home, my family resides in me, my hands are hands, feet, feet. Why revise reality and order detail so that salient little ripples show the origin of spring, the bound and bank of rivulets; why plant a childhood fantasy so as to dig it up? If man were judged by words, or deeds, there would be far less face cream in this land.

Perdition prance attendance on the devotee of ease; thy votary, a neophyte, knows shame. Presume no more upon my praise; Diana is not changeable as you. Devour every remnant of this adulation spent; the feast is finished, bones are picked, and, skeletal, I go. There was a little dancer and his name was Do-si-do.

115

To be eternal is to own ubiquity in time; the white whale swam in two concurrent seas. Discover your Northwest Passage (green grass growing over me); follow the Kodiac zodiac bear. We could wish to know permanence, Ponce de León; we should like to live transfigured, fixed. Elliptical insults sound in my skull, reverberate past all remembered praise and pleasantry, remain. That man can imitate a cock and this one horses; that one cooks. Plastered to some mental wall, the fire-lighted figures seem articulated frieze; rapt, we are perpetuated, pose.

To meditate, to mediate between the I and other, to sway straitened-circumstantial on a bench and eat of the flowering wheat (while frogs take a splash-oh, a bash-oh in pool), to know us evanescent, ever nascent, ever (over Roger and) out, cast of the islands molded by chance, contour of water our true landscape, shape, for octoroons with long skirts, legs, rise high above my grave (where they underneath wear, 'ware, no clothing at all)—a Saint inVites us, dance. There is no escaping thy final embrace, the last light convulsion and sport-spurt of breath. There is no refusal permitted us always, no compromise fully unmade. I watched a spider kill a bee above my table, page. Follow the straight gait and narrow the way; the sevenfold path has been folded; we must make our maiden-beds, lie; you must have your ticket stump stamped.

Adrift, adrift, the blood-dimm'd tide; Le Fever lies ill-tended; thy fire a falsified lighthouse, mock port, nor can we now moor more. The prodigal is written, and Narcissus also; what rough

beast slouches through this three-ring circus next? Stand me
now and ever in good stead, you laral laurels, pawned penates;
inseminate by artifice the orifice, sound depths.

Perhaps it was that you denied the deep tenacity of reason, its
depth, hold. Equilibrium and symmetry are basic to our stance,
and when we move what miracles of balance go unnoticed—
see, the young man carbuncular arrives. This vagary is but a
posture as the others (erratic, erotic, we pose), mastering of
stasis and a mustered poise.

Administered emetic empties the splenetic man; words have
led him wandering into this purge regurged. It is over now;
our dancer can perceive the dance while grief is grown
mechanical (*Wilkommen, wilkommen, süsser Bräutigam*), in-
verted, introverted, and so rudely forc'd.

Sullied with the sly absurdity of anger, we expunge. Incapable
of cleansing, we grow oiled, gross, old. Be all my sins remembered; the queen takes but one bath a year. What, my pretty
ones grown flaccid that were flaxen-haired, the dam at one fell
swoop gone dim, her retina (that held a retinue) detached?

Niobe was transformed to stone; is that preservation or absence
of grief? These are marble tears that stipple her unchanging
cheek, and that uncertain cry, suspended, cannot bring release.
Song snatches dominate my mind; heels click beneath my fibula
and ballet girls bridge to my nose. Plagued by a counterfeit

117

calm, I concentrate on ash, the ebony holder, hope, kirsch. Repose is but equivalence of tension, stasis now. The black magician, in his cave, holds power incommensurate with space, and it is important if he wake or weep. The exile that I am, however, self-proclaimed pariah, institutes no action but regret. The communal expiation that I alone accept is false; Astrid was not murdered, merely fell. And this long dirge is chanted for enchanted youth (our past upon that pyre, Pyrex, flames, brief candle flutters, gutters, wax waned) gone, conjured into pigs. Cato the Younger, forty-eight, had outlived all his friends. If senility assured redemption, that quiescent sainthood of the very young survived, why then we could progress, regress without unction or salve.

As a multicolored poster passes through the stages of its green, red, yellow uniformity and is four versions of a single block, as blue-that-is-soon-to-be-brown suggests its own extinction yet the eye remains, I can claim identity with my prefigured self. Lautrec used a toothbrush to paint; Alcuin of York wore fur, taught school, is not resurrected, stays dead. "Oscar can adopt himself to any situation"—take it from the champ, pile Pelion on Ossa, note the moving twigs that are caterpillars (Alcuin has been for eons bone), and watch chameleons, adapt.

Sometimes, in the simplest of senses, and now is one such time, I think myself unreal. Who, not altogether broken, would thus bewail this while? Who but a leashed dog would bay at the moon; who but a whupped pup would heel? Heal: for my poor fool is dead. Cohered, congealed in sentiment, I canonize the cannon, campaigning in adversity, left to the loom, to weave. Versus: A dialogue of shelf and rack: which has the nail, the screw?

Carp, carp, cavil, critic, cut; crave cravenly a middle and end, resumption, presumption of character, bloom from each plant (I know now why Van Gogh used yellow; it defies elaboration, has no outside border but black); critic, have you watched the carp converge upon thrown bread? I met a man and took his name but never saw him more. I know a thought which brought no fruition, a day which was twenty-four hours, and passed. I shall grow a beard, shall be poor and pariah, shall wear only sackcloth and asses can bray. Chance whelms, o'erwhelms us quite, and into the determined sea still holding to helm we are tossed. Palinurus, be my guide; describe the little fishes and the briny billow-pillow; comfort me with dapples, for I am sick above.

The saints of modern art have merged with silence, learned to

Empirical empire dominates hope: French soldiers made tents of dead horses in that Russian winter, crawled in. Aborted lay their every nascent aspiration, joy; urinating, defecating, we fold effluvia in cardboard, shape a book. Complacence and complaisance line our shelves in shovelfuls; what is allegorical in gore?

By this constant clatter-chatter I keep courage at the sticking place; by this colander I drain the remnant calendar and trick.

119

Company means after all but bread taken together; we prefer, please, cake. Unfit for decent human intercourse, I insist the light be on—residue of parents, of father's momentary missive-mission to the heathen depths, brought forth in judgment and sentenced to life, I wait my term-time, turn. Perhaps next royal birth or Coronation Day, we shall receive reprieve; perhaps my wife will come. Not bloody likely, sang sanguine Gwynn, for at her heel is Achilles', at her head twelve stone.

The boat named Semektet attains the dread Fifth Region, passes fierce Sokar. The goddess disappears, gives way to the Abyss of Waters, Sixth Realm of the Dead. Within that vast expanse, observe an osprey soar; we are the meek inheritors of dearth. Isis shall protect and guide, shall steer past deep weed banks.

Through bright concupiscence of courting we found, sounded no note amiss. Beneath the lilacs, lemon tree, we played the flute, lute, lout. Dance as puppets on a light sun-string; married, tied to virtue, yet shall man engender vice.

Adulation knows no confluence with honesty, congruence of object and its abject fawning imager, knows no limit to the formulaic: excess is success. Hypocrite, semblable to a lecturer, grows critical when adjectives extend; what a lackey language we construct to compliment. Complement thy daily bread with Grace.

There are those who make of each activity a ritual, who ponder and approach each problem as a test, for whom the length of line must be exactly accurate and pocketings immaculate and every answer weighed. The wasps are sluggish now and fall for no reason, for ease. Style is sanctuary when the subject fails.

Parent and child in one and at once, the husband cannot quit the wife nor wife the husband, spurning easily (the falcon cannot see the falconer) accord of chord, heart, hearth. Carlotta and Maximilian twined tendril-like to marble, and in an alien land. We hold to what is ours, we reach for what is falling; demotic, despotic, we diet on dotage, remain.

This is a difficult thing, impossible perhaps, to start at the end and retrace (post-prophetic, no hope of success), to hold no conception of the yet-to-come, to live a life thus fragmented, such work, for all roads lead to roam, and where hides organized intelligence, what cranny of this comedy, in which nook look for balance, where the principal? A stableboy, halt Hercules, who labors forever at Augean dung makes more ordureorder than I. For single steps forward, I must make two back, for each coin proffered must forge twenty-three. Disgust with digression, my falsified self (the governor sure had a way with his words, whipped his wards), overrides.

Exegesis (the Bible being exhausted), extends its fourfold prescient effort to our present lineage and line. The knee-high nihilists display such disarray—jejune beneath the juniper, a torrent of skirts to rent, rend. The ox knoweth his owner, and the ass his master's crib.

After such withdrawal, who could come away cold turkey; the anatomy of anesthesia is anathema. I exude you to exclude you, suppurate to separate, forge till I forget. Denuded of possession and deluded into imminence, this rambling dithyramb, odd ode, this effluence of fluency shall bubble, babble, end.

The several components of courage have always seemed discordant to me, often seem disjunct. How reconcile conscience with strength, resolution with thought; how abrogate bravura in the truly brave? Deny that cruelty which was the ancient's vice and you do disservice to the cause of faith. Desecrate no temple and you do not fall attended; Samson, guest, took hosts with him in death. Watch the tern pluck berries; watch the tern kill clams. The king in a chess game, unshadowed at noon, can cover three bishops by four.

Precision can shade into petulance, warp a man to infancy, distract him with detail, corrode. Apprentice to a vanished craft, hunter of pawnshops and haunter of boats, with no great ability, future, or luck, bending to hammer his hand—I know that poor preserve. What wall has he constructed that does not constrict?

Physician, heal thigh, pelf. The ostentation of our privacy is a taunt-flaunt worse than any smirking public man may register, proclaim. Privilege, insistent, stakes its stake, owns air. What could be less accurate than that men are born free—we come tied to the belly and womb. Rings enclose our fingers, clasp; the child who does not cry, physician, does not breathe.

I had not thought myself thus malcontent to age, so little able to forget, so willing to forgive. Belief in continuity has so seduced, traduced me that I hold no power to complete. The instinct of possession stands one with jealousy; we would throw much more out but for the fear of travelers who feast upon the waste. Each man who visits with you is a jackal, vulture, dog. Each proposal offered sounds an insult to disposal; each soft word they whisper-whimper echoes in my ear. The carnival is over, yet firm flesh continues well. (To you who wax melodious, give ear: cacophany of cat and birdcall breaks the silence merely, cannot shape it, sing. Passing through Pré-du-Lac, I heard a harpsichord, stopped, watched my father play. He missed each second note, knew nothing of the score, shut eyes, and, unintentional, played variations on a theme—but I delighted, would delight to sit at his feet, reverence. There was more music in his too-thick hand than any flattened disc; they played a cello suite beside his open grave. Larks rock along the telephone wire, lift their tails, drop beaks; I shall tell you my theory of art. We must saw at the unbroken string.)

Adjust the teeth upon your gums and mouth: we are renewed. What effulgence of indulgence sets me, still, to type?

The pendulum of partnership swings back, forth, back, forth, back; we yet insist it possible that two might share, divide. There must be reciprocity above the watershed; passion must somewhere meet passion, its sole equivalence, and know reprieve, respite.

The dismembered Dionysus floats within a lifted glass and thyrsi wreathed with branches wave where pine cones crackle, wild grapes wind. Women beat with heavy heels upon the matted ground and fall on it as mattress, tear their temples' linen free. Drinking the miracle draught as a fish, retaining through gills their residual past, wheeling with Ixion guiding the flight plan, dancing for Tantalus slow tarantelles, the Bacchantes surrender and rend.

Paradise is many places, say the Moslem, Creek and Greek. I have sat at *Heaven's Gate* and eaten in *Elysium;* the single certain thing is this: angel food will fill no stomach, nectar quench no thirst. Every skin plucked from the table of grace is grudged, anointed, torn; every limb boiled in the vat of contrition is fleshless, fat and crust.

Echo, Astrid, has no purpose but reply; her bones are changed to rock. (Profoundly lost, profound) purple within and white without, the flower of young manhood wilts; it was predicted thus. I should have been a ragged clause, old man with wrinkled divisions, not caught in this rippling parenthesis, not sated with satyriasis, mirror of a drowned self, marred. Triapin is accurate, though eyeless: I embrace reflection, watch the fountain, fall.

Palm leaves fringe the folded sky above Aruba, starched and uniform; beringed, the maiden, marketing, is sweetest bloom to see. Tropes slope ever to the tropics, porpoise leap with purpose there, *et in Arcadia ego.* Bear the scented brand above you to the sea; fish leap toward that light.

Love is no private inscape, promontory never scaled nor instress ill-explained; every mother's son stands testimonial.

Felicity has also had her history. How simple to assume that we are isolated, insulated, that the grass has not been previously pressed, that this sand was not receptable and sheet. Hunger, unappeased, has kept the female belly full.

Prince, do not inquire why the horn and zither noise that Aphrodite out of Cythera is come. She spreads, the soft resounding deity of snow, her blanket by your side. She, the inconsolable, asks aid. Walk with her on hillocks that aspire to be hills; coal piled high is higher than that tree.

Apathy has altogether maimed the hand of hope; gratitude is expectation, not a debt redeemed. All the world's theatrical, but the producer left us, and nobody can direct. Improvisation, Antonin, is cruelty, art-oh. The manner of our matter will produce a fund of form and steel the audience to style, inform.

(Soar to the edible stars and nibble on their nacreous rim till nausea is the property of others, of the state. Getting and spending our days are laid waste; the world is too much withal.) When once the primitive absorbs perspective, laws of distance, he grows civilized. Sophistication is the background brought to play, and cynicism is the foreground lost to view. When we truly know banality as ours (this, a book of common prayer, place), each ideal is vanished and all aspiration fled.

Stimulate or simulate desire, strut unclothed; April mixes lilac and quinine; trumpet, strumpet, sound reveille, breed, bleed. As artistry is honesty, so honesty is art. Imperious, impervious, avid or pavid, we swap our stories (darn good yarn, crayon rayon), knit wit and wash our mouths with lye.

Crescent-shaped, the seeds of paradox still flower; water falls where no ear hears; Clytie, the sun plant, follows her god. I write these words foreknowing that you neither read nor understand; I yet address to you this false shared memory. We have seen the plastic bottles float like geese.

There are some battles it is better not to fight. There is some choice still offered to us, shield. (Note, notes, monotonous motto, ten months now of self-indulgence, speech; jest in gestation, geste, funereal rite; a period of mourning taxed, imposed. Or is it less legitimate even, self-subjection, capitalized privacy, usage now as then?) Everything stands grist to the mill-maul, labyrinth, maize; we are but granules crushed.

(Parrots wheel and circle, squabble, perch near cactus, streak with rainbow panoply this sunset of the mind. What gentle and capturing hand will tether, cage me, offer shade; what keeper will strew boards with seed? Have you heard a purpose taper into prose, heard the old men shrill themselves to sleep?)

Let us discuss the fallacy of following that which refuses to lead. Let us imagine next a fallow field repelling proper seed. Thousands volunteer for the rank of private in some squalid squadron, cause, live their ladder-livelihood strung to the bottom rung. Observe the jackass-of-all-trades, the permanent apprentice, the talentless devotee and devout habitué; he hath supplicated, suppurated that these hurts might heal; he hath suppered, suffered with the army of defeat.

Astrid, Astrid. (A certain Mr. Vanderhupe parading in the park at Menton, cane beneath his left gloved hand, umbrella in his right, observed to a news dealer there that it was a fine day. This latter individual, magnanimous, agreed.)

Mystics make disunion hell and (watch that missile pierce, push, thrust through sky) sorrow disengagement. Feet drift like plankton on sea. Use of the vernacular implies nor kinship nor cozenage, kind; my mouth shaped as yours is not identity.

For one week now it lay contained, restrained, the need to squander and syllabify, essay, assay, assail. In the limpid water limpets cling and my mind ripples ease. A seal came to the village harbor, harbinger of ice. (Elude allusion and elide derision; Elysian romps on rumps are but a fond illusion; we live shackled to the everlasting sticks. All those tales about eternity being sand in a bird's beak and mountains are wrong: it is this pretty pity and one instant by instinct possessed. He had a head for figures, and she had no head.)

What travesty of virtue is this sham yea-saying, upraised arm, an invitation, invocation to forgetfulness, each initiate gone vitiated, dull. Commitment should apply to institutions only, and to mental institutions first. *Fürst*, is that a doge, dog, dowager you see before you, staggering? Send for the attendant furs and furze.

127

Dance the *souche* dance, twisted as the vine root, bent, imaging fertility until it cannot fail, recreating genesis from Dionysus crushed. Grapes burst, are drunk, are sown, spring forth. Even from the soot is man engendered, organized; I have walked on wine until thigh, foot are drunk.

In Castellane Ut-napishtim has not walked, remote. By the waters of the fountain Gilgamesh sat, wept. From respect of your sobriety, I should renounce this joke. Urshanabi gave conduct safely through the sea of Death. Before the nine days were completed and the plant prepared, a serpent came and ate.

We are the most uncritical of audiences, readily moved by some mawkish performance, engaged in the troubles of sweet sister Susan, indentured servants to the current set of dentures, caught by the bathos of song or of terror, borne on the wings of a tortoise, pleased with abortions of art. The sky is filled with lamentation, electrical sunsets, exhaust.

A triolet for two, a quartet of tinned guava jelly and elastic fastener; Adrasteia made with Chronos sky. The pantomimic gestures of a man behind his window move me as no conversation could; divorce of thought and its component parts gives bankrupt speech that, coined, cannot longer purchase tribute, is a mute abused. This could continue, cyclic, with no happy ending, and our popcorn would be butterless before projectors dim. A drunken man, Aristippus, weaved down the winding sheet of street, through penny-farthing purgatories he considered hell.

Into angularity the circle comes as comfort; between two pints and a straight line stretches irregular distance; stolid geometry buckles to chaos, relieved. In each allegory, remember, you can find a gory leg; with the birth of beauty there is blood.

Old men in the park play chess and cackle as they castle, queen a pawn. Henry the Eighth pawned a gaggle of queens, and was an old man also, indistinct. When this year is over, all, Astarte, shall start as before; regeneration is the constancy of Re. Break like light into this bridled bed (*nel mezzo del* mucked-up *cammin*) and illustrate devotion, finger Rosy, dawn. Janus, the two-faced god, knows no lateral vision, is blinded to breadth (and I, escaped, am only come again to Carthage); see, the ruin, punitive, and I alone—through tangled banks and wild sea wind—atone.

Incarnadined, that western lake reflects the passing of pink majesty, cold memory of flame. There was no murder, death, nor love portrayed within great Epidaurus; therefore I don a mask, reed pipe, and voice the fact of nothing, act the oral-choral part. Heat, too, is a comparative; we know our Eden afterwards; Lot's wife was a poet, looked back.

Night is a great bat's wing that subjugates the room. These are the sounds that resound in the echoing arch of a skull. We found a skeleton, uncovered by erosion, prayerful, hands spread

129

before the socket of its nose, gap-toothed. Mute counselor of reconciliation, it awaited air.

Squeezing clustered bitterness from my acerbic self, aping past prophets of simian night, seeing in each sunset repetition merely, reaping the profits of wind—promiscuity has thus annulled, annealed me; Anu, also Ea, were afraid.

Watch the viscous fluid flow from your adoring cup; know that some sufficient feast shall destroy detritus, nourish, cradle, rock. Split milkweed waits expectant for the wind: I shall subjugate disunity, curtail the tale, contain. Within those scuttling ragged claws the chitin turns to chiton, works anew.

Atreus of song and story brought the silver chalice smiling to his lip. Harp, ye harpies, on the dignity of grief and on that regicide before us who hath stained the crown. We all are tributaries to the river Wrun. Had Orestes three such sisters, added to the furious nine, he would have stayed crazed after Aulis, gone whooping to the water, bled, sought no sanctuary, settled with the outcast of this earth.

Slave makes master captive in his kindly office, audience. Brother lies beset by brother where proud honor stakes the plain. Dandelions wither on their wormlike stalks, droop, sow. Love has pitched his palace by my Caelia's remnant rump. Six slow virgins bear the urn; Empedocles is minimal that once stood five-foot-nine.

130

Mutability is that which lacks the mute ability to hold. A mistaken mystique, *errare humanum,* our fixed illusion of flux. The farmers now own real estate, not land. How all occasions do inform; inconstancy stands constant, Sisyphus lies down.

After the first death, there is no ether. After the held breath, we feel release. See, he comes, bright keys ajangle, locked doors opening. And in some simple correlation, sun ariseth, day. (Art as chaos come to order is a platitude. Concomitance of opposites exists within each model; modal uniformity is rare. In paragraph, conception, phrase, the random and the rigid equally pertain. All authors order and are ordered, institute and execute, anticipate the accidental stimulus, reap, rope.)

This plate is peopled with the most fantastical of figures, centaur and centurion, nymph, turk, Turgenev. Threnody of thrashes with a willow rod for staff, elegy of closing what is circular, won't end—andante, too, is dust. Which intervention of invention can redeem my fictive theme; *passacaglia* of pity, proceed.

Pomegranates scar the mouth and shape it into gallantry, the succulence of gall. Sardonic herbs are poisonous, a rictus stretched to smile. Eros sleeps a seeming serpent, keeps the lamp unlit. Smoke executes an arabesque against umbrella pines; piper tracks embroider this perimeter of sand. Upon that sine curve described by the manic-depressive, the wave that patterns each oscilloscope and tide, between those common complements, passivity, aggression, we form a set and zero sum, a canceled remainder, flat field. A car, gears stripped, is neutral merely, cannot reverse, nor is there forward incline on a plain.

Recitative turns the audience restive, summons disbelief. Synthetic fibers of a story go unraveled here, the country seems untraveled and my mirrored nature dim. What is he that walks beside you? Those who hold no expectation cannot keep concern. Pacify Pasiphaë where she awaits you, dread and red. Cover bare Queen Catherine; ingratiate, ingrate. A virgin touches, tames the unique horn; dredge for scallops only where the wildebeest won't go.

Dahak, when evil forces reign, shall be released from Damavand; fetterless, the story says, he will kill all but Keresaspa, and in turn be slain. Then, and only then, as once with Faridun, can we envision comfort, will we live in peace. Above me oleander blooms; somehow I still hear sheep.

One dog will find the once-locked limbs of scattered partnership. Death is dark beginning, merely, wheel within a wheel. From his mound a brier grew and from her mound a weed. Graves, they say, cannot stay shut beneath that questing paw. Relic of lost symmetry, the hand seeks hand, heart, heart.

From indolence to insolence, each of the five senses blighted, we slip with studied ease, see trees no longer studded with their springtime crescent color and the millrace clogged with

meal, perch, rock, think back to ceremonial dinners and innocence drowned, a six-dollar cigar where there used to be smoke.

Khepri the Renewer sleeps within strong serpent coils; Neferka
the Scribe chants salutation nonetheless; his father, as a consequence, gains sight. Pass before me now in all your pagan
majesty and our grief were redeemed. The seventh hour passes,
and there is no risen Re—a bearded lion looms.

What new form, a petal folding, offers substance forth as seed,
is seminal, reality's harvest, veil torn? What insemination more
than artifice pertains; why couple word against word? The
canceled check that language is augurs silence, bankrupt
speech; they that enter this deep swamp subside, anonymous. I
construct Penelope as an apposite image, spider's scrawled web
—not for her fidelity but for her fruitless art, the night's renunciation of day's shuttle, loom. We all are tapestries, enwrought,
undone, reduced to carpet, pet. The sideboard splinters, door
creaks in wind; skeins of straw geese, pinned to the wall, ravel
to the desk's horizon, cease. The truth is very hard to tell and
very unimportant to a man with arthritis and eight children,
hate; even that mythic unnoticing figure I manage to romanti-
cize, applaud his lack of clap. Graffiti have been read as long as
Aesop, and this hieroglyph of need should translate into deed,
not rhyme. Beauty is a fleeting thing but readily renewed, a boy
forever, masque in stock; with wax depilatories we deface.

In Draguignan at dead of night Ishtar might well walk un-
molested, nor would any mortal reverence. Man leers, cigar in

teeth, at every passing perjury of greatness, every dead joy resurrected, skeleton preserved. Into Irkalla, whence Tammuz had preceded her, Ishtar descended also, ate the dust and mud.

This city is evil, a sea-squall and rudderless ship, a sequel to the old saltpetered pilloried towns, a parody of shelter and a market place for fools. Between the bridge and river hangs that vast suspension, void; call volcanic retribution on their easiness. With horror listen to the banter, bartering: "My wife for your husband, quits."

By Plascassier I pondered the significance of Calca; clouds moved colorless in far severity of sky; Shadow-of-a-Lance lay stilled upon her bed. Huayllapampa overshadows stones that once breathed, ran; I deem myself pre-eminently bone. Cloak, become the woman that is gone.

Through a wood of birch and maple, thick fern forest strewn with oak, past a beaver dam and bog, a stone wall wound, three feet throughout. Laid by a man and mule at seven cents per yard in 1843 (town records called him Abner, son of Clarence Bottlewright, but did not name the mule), symmetrical still, precise without purpose, ordaining what was pasture once and what was crop, now both pine beds, the wall, obsidian-seeming and useless, stretched beyond where we could walk it, imaged life, *Angst,* art. Acquiescent, I continue, pen the penal year, wonder is it clear that I had hoped for reconstruction, buttoned back my brown corduroy's fly. This book was twelve months in the writing and the separation, twelve; it is now the lawyer's province, will contract. The water trickles through the toilet as an imitative stream; Georges sharpens scythes again, will barber the meadow for spring.

The largest mausoleum, weather-beaten, fades; the little graven stone stands etched against all wind. The lobster as a poet sheds, its secret shell secretes. In water where blue blades dip white, you too can catch a crab. Condescension is the worst of every oversight.

The sacrament of excrement spreads wholly through the land; we defecate, desecrate, sing. Perimeter of wire must enclose the passion now; sextons have their rifle and bellpull. Faith, rope, and charity, that august trio, tripartite tree, declines in September to blossom, gives leave.

The iterated protestation of eternity, assurance of "always," "forever," "undying"—the permanence of passion being chalked on every school slate, carved on every tree—an endless insistence on ease without end neglects the primal principle of change, translates, betrayed, to self-betrayal and the statement: now is all. How many stand seduced by transcience, plead for repetition merely, think that growth, progression is at best exchange. I was young, will be old, was content once, am not; yet, in that final nodding dotage, day-dowry perseveres.

Again I see continuum in what is disconnected, series and set theory in the first flawed factors grouped, a sequence in inconsequence ("ah men!" in each farewell), patterns, preformed, plausible, that need not signify, delirium of atomies within that cycle, trend; a negative times negative is pus. Intelligence puts eight after a two-four-six; imagination—five. Swift called a fishwife "isosceles triangle"; debased, she wept and fled.

Here, in this lute-*lutte,* are ninety-five theses of protest contained, forty-one errors included, indulgence, a diet of worms, bullfinch among the rushes, reed, plangent tangent, plaited plaint. You are a vanishing point, something more than kin, and perspective is attained.

Alouate, the howling monkey, disdains agaves, aloe (our house, *A Louer*). Completion is not longer to be feared. Connascency of gentleness with distance, kindness with true unconcern, spreads wed within one brain; all your wit and grace are sundered, bearable; these sententious sentences diminish to parole.

Novel descending a staircase, plasm-spasm, renegade; dissemble, disassemble, Roland holds his breath. *Preux chevalier,* stretched beneath a mackerel sky, where the rocks at Roncevaux are pallet, marker: rest. Thrice you were requested to relent, three times sought release. The hills reverberate with praise, a dying blast, and sound is bound for vengeance, Paris, home.

Pre-eminent among the sons of men moved Harry with his leg chain for a wristband, Ephraim with his tarpaulin for tie. Mallets formed their knuckles and two basketballs their sex;

valleys were indented when and while they trod the sod. Climb carefully down yonder ridge; it once was Ephraim's thigh.

All experience is either known or comprehended, capable of application to the tablet, bruise. Sculpt and lime, lock joints on the chisel, seal your floating reverie within a stele of steel. Irrelevance need not be mere irreverence; intelligent revelry can but reveal; resist the block poem (almost successfully), head.

Obsessed with the inadequate, I hear half voices, scorn. There are those who disapprove of long inaction, life. Every day we dither and we wither every way. Can you not look kindly on this slow convulsion, upturned crab (nature raw in maw and claw): watch the pairs of feet, no longer fetal, futile, kick. Alchemy increases the spiritual content of lead.

The person on business from Porlock requests an audience.

Yet formalities of fiction (to tell a lie, a story, untruth, homily) seem but a worn mime, gambit, game. I do not care to shroud the object in its specificity, correlate my coffee spoons and mermaid, forge an accidental death or meeting, labor love or conversation, outline snout and moles. Aristotle said to not compare a tree and cheese, but we are grown exhausted with the effort of distinguishing till every pigeon holds.

The wind from Norway and the wind from Borneo are borne together buffeting the sandbag of this skull. Split rampart in the

137

rampant night of what is last, and lasting; sing beneath the ripe rip tide your scale. There was a little swimmer and his name was Her-aye-oh; sand sharks leaped as brown and high as he.

I am aquiver with illusion, pregnant with expectancy, a dog in pursuit of that boomerang-bone, Sisyphus commencing assent, a flower in middle-march thaw. What mannerist mistake is this to think that perne may equal gyre, start again as rise? What manner of hyperbole in our described hyperbola could lead me to believe an axis might be altered, foci changed? We are not forgiven our sons. Something less than absolution, a solution—father, find me that.

Periodicity demands some punctuation of these days, persists in differential, sees the iris die. Wax flowers can confute the calculus of motion; wax your face, outface. The dandy stoops to gather dandelion seed, a thing of pure impermanence, remains.

Children drag a Christmas tree out of the tended pile; women brandish branches at the insult of such incandescence, cry for that respect the vagrant pay to vacancy, warn of retribution in swift blindness, madness, tiger teeth. Could I meet my mother, would I tear the remnant festival thus from her incompetence and bear as garland back the whip wound of her dumb-struck tongue? They say a god came welcomed when my father was not home.

In Roquebrune Hrothgar might build his hall, give rings and mead; Heorot resounded with the gay prelude to doom. Birds

138

of passage are we, beating at barn windows and unmindful of the door. Keep, you fond retainers, all the booty I have earned; the very wing of morning has been bloodied, torn by time.

We have placed the entrails of our deity in pots, have drained and boiled the fluids of his elbow, kidney, lung. My fifth metacarpal was once strung to glory, my tongue can but echo, invoke. Born from that disjunction we forge imitative masses and from that dismemberment we hazard unity. A plow can harrow circles in resilient earth; stones bore silent witness to his hard division, death.

I have come back. The snow still is dust on the crest of these mountains (just time, the only pretty ring on these mountains again); it is the start of the spring. Waiting for me, you wear, as remembrance, the white dress that you once would wear. O'er the green cornfield did pass ill-lit processionals, illicit professionals; forgive; you will not follow now nor lead.

—*Grasse, 3/23/66*—